Performa
HOOF
Performance
HORSE

Performance
HOOF
Performance
HORSE

Nic Barker

J.A. ALLEN

First published in 2017 by
JA Allen

JA Allen is an imprint of
The Crowood Press Ltd
Ramsbury, Marlborough
Wiltshire SN8 2HR

www.crowood.com

British Library Cataloguing-in-Publication Data
A catalogue record for this book is available from the British Library.

ISBN 978 1 90880 970 4

For Ghost, Felix, Charlie and Bailey who taught me my
first lessons, and Angel, Dexter and Jack who continued
my education.

The extract from *Beyond Words – what animals think and feel* by Carl Safina is
reproduced with his permission. The quote from Kim Walnes's blog *The Way of the
Horse* is used with her permission. All photographs are the author's unless indicated
otherwise.

Disclaimer
While this book is as accurate as the author can make it, there may be omissions or
errors. The publisher and author cannot accept responsibility for loss or damage
caused directly or indirectly by the information contained in this book.

Typeset by Jean Cussons Typesetting, Diss, Norfolk

Printed and bound in India by Replika Press Pvt Ltd

Contents

Acknowledgements

This book could not have been written without the advice and help I received from my fellow hoof enthusiast Steve Leigh (with whom I have filmed hooves, brainstormed about hooves and obsessed about hooves), and my extraordinary veterinary friends, Becca Hart and Freya Brookes, who have pored over data, answered questions and kept me more or less on the straight and narrow. The mistakes are my own.

My heartfelt thanks go to every single owner who has ever decided to give that crazy barefoot idea a chance and send their horses to Rockley for rehabilitation, and all those who have read the blog or joined us on social media over the years. Most of all, my gratitude goes to all the horses who have made me think, opened my eyes, and inspired me with their ability to grow better hooves than I ever imagined.

Rockley Farm, March 2017

Foreword

As a veterinary surgeon, owner and rider, I have learnt a huge amount about whole-horse health from Nic. Her logical, practical approach makes physiological and ethical sense.

My own horses have been kept to the principles explained in this book for several years. They compete successfully in British Eventing and British Dressage, and follow hounds. They are sounder, have cleaner legs and are better prepared to handle variations in terrain and ground conditions.

Dr Rebecca Hart BvetMed, MRCVS

CHAPTER 1

Rock-Crunching Hooves

Recently I broke the rules.

Andy and I were going away, for the first time in ten years, and for the first time in ten years we only had our own horses to worry about. It was a warm, mild, mellow autumn and we wanted to make life as easy as possible for the friends who were looking after the horses while we were away. We left the horses with access to the tracks (*see* Chapter 4), a feeder full of haylage, and forty acres of grass to do with as they wished – no restrictions on where they went or what they ate, and no formal exercise for three weeks.

It might have sounded risky, but when we got home the horses were in fantastic condition and, most importantly, had the same rock-crunching feet they had when we left. I didn't really expect anything else – after all, I wouldn't gamble with the health of our horses – but it was an interesting affirmation of something I have been exploring for several years now: that great hooves, healthy hooves, aren't that difficult to maintain, nor do they need much in the way of human intervention.

A healthy hoof is a normal state of affairs for a healthy horse.

I will say from the start that throughout this book, when I talk about healthy hooves, it means hooves that are totally sound, capable of covering mile after mile on all sorts of terrain, day after day, at all paces without shoes. I am well aware that hooves like this don't happen by accident, certainly not in a domestic environment. On the contrary, we are used to seeing unhealthy feet as the norm on many, perhaps most, of the horses we see day to day. Given that so many of us begin our hoofcare journeys with horses that have unhealthy feet, it is perhaps not surprising that it can often feel as if achieving a healthy hoof is an impossible struggle, and that there are obstacles and challenges continually in the way.

The obstacles and challenges that we face when hooves are unhealthy are real, and I am not belittling them in the slightest, but it is important not to lose sight of the fact that a healthy hoof is what the horse is always trying to grow – it is the default position, and not some impossible dream. A healthy hoof is a normal state of affairs for a healthy horse.

ACHIEVING HEALTHY HOOVES

So why are healthy hooves so difficult for many of us to achieve with our horses? It's not that we are bad owners, nor is it that we pick the wrong horses – and it's not even (usually) down to bad luck. It's more often the case that our horses are living in an environment that makes healthy hooves difficult to achieve.

Over the last decade there has definitely been an increasing awareness on the part of horse owners about what affects hooves, good and bad, and I'd like to think I have played a part in that. In *Feet First*, which I started writing with Sarah Braithwaite in 2007, we introduced the idea that there is a 'holy trinity' of nutrition, exercise and environment, and that these form the key elements of hoof health – and this is something I still stand by today.

However, it was undoubtedly true then, and I think it remains common today, that those who are the most interested in hoof health are usually those who have the most to gain – in other words, those whose horses have (or had) problem feet. After all, human nature being what it is, if you have a horse with robust feet that never cause you a moment's worry, then you will almost certainly never expend too much thought on those feet. This had the inevitable effect that, initially at least, the owners who were most interested in barefoot were owners whose horses were lame, which typically were shod, and where both owner and horse were running out of options.

There is no doubt that for many of these horses, getting the 'holy trinity' right and going barefoot was enormously beneficial. There are very many horses today, and we will never know exactly how many, who have been given, quite literally, a new lease of life when they would otherwise have faced ongoing lameness and euthanasia. There is also no doubt that bringing horses like these back to soundness is a tough job.

You are usually dealing with a foot that has had years of being compromised and weak – in many cases (perhaps in most cases) a foot that has never been truly healthy. It doesn't take much imagination to realize that with unhealthy hooves like these, which are precariously edging towards soundness and strength you have very little margin for error. Taking hooves like these barefoot gives the feet the best chance, in my opinion, of strengthening and improving – but it is not a magic wand, and many of these horses will have had such severely compromised feet that, even when they have improved barefoot, a complete return to soundness is not possible.

With compromised feet you need to be extremely careful with nutrition, surfaces, and the work the horse is doing. That is why the sort of regime I described at the start, which suited my horses admirably, is not something I could ever risk with the horses who come here, with weak feet, for rehabilitation. Once a horse has healthy feet, though, he finds it easy to maintain them – he will be comfortable on his own feet, so tough terrain is not an issue for him, and he goes where he chooses. My horses were preferring to spend a proportion of their time on the tracks, and in the shelter of the woods and barns, as opposed to being in a soft, wet field 24/7, and so they were also voluntarily spending part of each day off the grass.

When they were grazing, even during the day, it did them no harm, partly because our grass is 'safe' – it is not artificially fertilized, but is managed organically, with a huge diversity of plants rather than a mono-culture of a single species – but there is also the fact that their feet have been tough, strong and hard-working for many years, and their hooves have an inherent fitness now which protects them as well.

When you see horses with perfect hooves moving at speed over tough terrain there is an ease, a confidence that is almost a swagger, and an elegance in their gaits which is something I have never seen in a shod horse. This unique quality of movement in horses with healthy hooves is the reason I will never use shoes on any of our own horses.

Often having a horse barefoot is seen as hard work, a challenge, and not for the faint-hearted – if you want to make life easy, then just bang a set of shoes on the horse. But it doesn't need to be like that. It should be a joy to see horses work barefoot – they should awe you with their sure-footedness, amaze you with their capability on tough terrain, and movement should look effortless for them.

Barefoot is all about balance: hooves are healthiest when horses are eating varied forage which is not intensively farmed, and when they are moving for most of their time, covering many miles in a day. Of course, this is also when horses are at their healthiest – but there is more. If we manage our fields in a way that is better for hooves, it is also better for biodiversity

It should be a joy to see horses work barefoot.

and wildlife. Barefoot is about balance, and if hooves are healthy there is a beautiful, virtuous circle which has benefits beyond the health and well-being of the horse.

It's true that taking a horse barefoot can be a great remedy for weak hooves, allowing them to develop the strength that shoeing has denied them, but if you have the choice it is much better – and easier – to allow your horse to grow great hooves from the start, and never to allow them to deteriorate to the point where they 'need' shoes. I see so many horses whose owners have to try barefoot because the only other option is to put the horse down because of ongoing lameness. I have nothing but respect and admiration for their commitment to their horses, and it is a huge thrill when their horses grow vastly healthier feet (as they mostly do) and come back into full work barefoot.

It's sad, though, that these horses – who invariably were born with better feet – have had to live with gradually deteriorating hooves, to the point when they actually go lame. Although barefoot is a great lifeline for hooves that are at the point of failure, how much better is it to help your horse grow the best possible hooves long before there is a problem.

DEVELOPING GREAT FEET

So why is a horse with outstandingly healthy, hardworking feet still a relative rarity? I believe it is often due to the ingrained belief that hooves are immutable – a part of the horse's conformation that is incapable of change. We are taught that hooves should be a pair, and that horses shouldn't have under-run heels or long toes. What we are not taught is that hooves can start off looking perfect, but can worsen over time – or conversely can be weak, and strengthen over time. Horses, and hooves, come in all shapes, sizes and conditions of health or sickness, and what you have today is not necessarily what you will have in six months' time, let alone in a year's time.

Many of us have had the satisfaction of bringing on a young horse – helping transform an unbalanced, inexperienced youngster into a fit and well-mannered adult horse. Equally many of us can probably recall horses (let's hope not our own) that have gone from being perfectly balanced and beautifully schooled to being unfit, tense or unwilling because of physical problems or poor treatment.

It's no different with the horse's feet – but a horse with 'terrible' feet is not necessarily something you have to accept. Even the thinnest-soled ex-racehorse, shod at eighteen months and with a totally under-developed palmar hoof, can grow a better foot. Barefoot is not a magic wand, and a horse like this will, realistically, never be able to overcome completely those early disadvantages – but why wait until this sort of horse has under-run hooves, mismatched feet and a poor landing? Far better to prioritize the job of improving those feet (because they *can* be improved) as soon as possible, and with luck avoid, or at least minimize, soundness problems before they raise their ugly head.

I hope that in the future developing great feet will become much more of a focus not just for owners on a day-to-day basis, but also for those who are bringing on young horses. Youngsters who are fed correctly and are, ideally, allowed to move on a variety of terrain rather than just soft flat fields, will have a head start when it comes to developing tough, strong, well balanced feet, and should be set up for a lifetime of soundness. However, even with horses like this, who have had a great foundation of good hoofcare, there is no room for complacency because healthy hooves aren't a fixed state, but an ongoing commitment – and even the best hooves are only as good as the horse's current diet, environment and workload.

Once these are in place and consistent, though, then you and your horse should be within that 'virtuous circle', where good hooves enable good movement, which enables correct work and great fitness, balance over all terrain, true sure-footedness, and a confidence and ease of movement which I believe you simply can't replicate in the shod horse.

As an owner, not only should you be proud of the hard work you and your horse have put into achieving this level of fitness and hoof health, but you also have the assurance of knowing that your horse is as healthy as he can be, that his movement is at its absolute best, and that his good biomechanics and well-balanced hooves should give him the best chance of a long, injury-free life. For me, this is what having a barefoot horse is all about.

Whereas *Feet First* was all about the basics of hoof health, the aim of this book is to go further and explore how we can achieve the best for our horses – training, managing and riding them in a way that enables them to grow fantastic feet, enhances their overall health, and which respects their needs as well as our own.

WHOLE HORSE HEALTH

This isn't a book just about feet, because feet are simply the magnifying glass. What I mean by this is that problems in the feet are usually a clue that there are wider problems that we need to address – perhaps in how we feed, perhaps in how the horse moves, perhaps in how we ride or train. The flip side is that if you have a horse with great feet, then you and your horse are probably doing a lot of things right.

Great feet are a confirmation of whole horse health, and poor feet are a warning of ill health – but if we are ambitious about the health and happiness of our horses we need to look much further than just the feet. So you can't talk about hooves without talking about biomechanics and nutrition and anatomy; you can't talk about management without looking at how the horse evolved and his physiology; and you can't talk about riding and working the horse without looking at how all these factors interact.

If that sounds like a minefield, don't worry. We can't be experts in all these fields – I certainly am not, and that isn't the aim of this book. Instead, my objective is to give you the tools for assessing your own horse, suggestions for making practical changes that make it easier for you to keep your horse at the top of his game, whatever that is, and some ideas for problem-solving if things go a bit wrong.

Good hooves enable good movement.

CHAPTER 2

Balanced Hooves, Dynamic Hooves

The traditional way of assessing horses' feet is to look at the static horse, but I hope to persuade you that there is a better way. By looking at the horse in motion and assessing the foot as it loads and lands we can, in my experience, learn a lot more than we ever can from a stationary hoof: after all, the horse's leg is not like a table leg (contrary to the opinion I once heard expressed by an equine vet) but has evolved to cover ground efficiently and at high speed.

By using this dynamic balance instead of static balance as a guide to the hoof we can find out whether a foot has the right dorso-palmar and medio-lateral balance, whether the horse is able to fully extend his limbs, whether he is using both limbs evenly, and whether there are any niggling discomforts which may lead to lameness or injury in the future.

DYNAMIC ASSESSMENT IS CRUCIAL

The difference between static and dynamic assessment is crucial because a foot only makes sense in motion. The horse evolved to travel large distances and be capable of high speed, and the function of the hoof is to enable this to happen as efficiently as possible.

There was a lot of comment back when our horses first started working barefoot about how (or whether) they would cope. People being only human, it was very rare (in fact unheard of) for someone to say 'isn't it amazing how well they do?' or, 'isn't it incredible how well hooves thrive on high mileage over tough terrain?' Much more frequent were pessimistic statements such as 'they'll get worn away on the roads', and 'it's all very well in the wild, but wild horses aren't ridden', and gloomy predictions that horses would never cope without shoes in the constantly wet British climate, but would quickly go lame.

The best way, in my experience, to deal with these annoying and prescriptive prophets of doom (opinions such as these are invariably voiced by 'experts' who have limited or no experience of barefoot horses) is, frankly, to ignore them and get the answers straight from the horse's mouth – or in this case, his feet.

Since those early days I've seen nothing to make me change my belief in what our horses have proved to me time and time again: that a truly healthy hoof is capable of covering miles and miles, day after day and year after year, no matter what the terrain. The huge advantage of being unshod is, of course, that the hoof has better shock absorption without the interference of metal. The other massive benefit is (potentially) perfect hoof balance – but how can you tell whether your horse's hooves are balanced? In fact it is simpler than you might think to assess hoof balance, as long as we bear in mind that hooves are not designed to stand still, they are designed to move.

It is much easier to look at hooves when horses are standing still, and so that is traditionally how we assess them – but in fact dynamic assessment is far more useful than static assess-

Hooves are designed to move.

ment, and movement is absolutely essential in order to judge whether a hoof is balanced. As I am sure you already know, the horse's hoof is anatomically a single toe which evolved to allow the horse the greatest possible speed, and so you need to assess a hoof not just on its own, but as part of the whole limb.

CONSIDER THE WHOLE HORSE

As well as this, we need to remember that, naturally, a single limb cannot work in isolation, and so we need to stand back and consider the whole horse, including his other three hooves, rather than look at one hoof at a time. This doesn't mean you need a PhD in equine anatomy before picking up a hoof, but you do need an appreciation of how the horse moves. You need to understand, for example, that a front limb lameness will always have a knock-on effect on the hind legs (which will often also have a related shortened stride), and it will also affect the muscles of the neck, back and shoulder. This will be apparent not only in the muscles that power and support the affected limb, but also in the muscles on the opposing side, where the limb may be forced to compensate.

   If your horse has one foot more upright than the other, it is a function of how he has been moving: as a rule the upright foot will be the one he has been loading less. Hoof conforma-

Hooves continually try to provide maximum support for the limb above.

tion is not set in stone, and even though hooves appear tough and unyielding, they are really plastic and malleable – their structure adapts and changes depending on how the horse is moving, landing and loading his feet.

When we look at hooves from our usual position, standing roughly level with the horse's head and looking down on the hoof from above, we see only the hard external hoof capsule, and it looks pretty solid. In fact the hoof wall is covering not only the pedal and navicular bones, but a complex and interconnected framework of tendons and ligaments as well as other critical structures such as the solar and frog coriums. The hoof also has an extensive blood and nerve supply, and is constantly receiving and relaying sensory information from and to the rest of the body.

The hoof is really one of the most adaptive parts of the whole limb, and it is brilliant at compensating for injury elsewhere. It can provide support for weaknesses not only in the hoof, but in other areas higher up the limb – for instance, you will often see deviations in the hoof as a result of hock arthritis or soft tissue damage, and I have even seen one instance of a hoof wall deviation which appeared to be a compensation for a pectoral injury.

From what I see of hardworking bare hooves, I am convinced that the hoof responds not just to the surfaces it is traversing and the mileage it is doing, but also to how the limb above is loading. It would make sense for hooves to be continually trying to provide maximum support to the limb above them, but they will only be able to do so if the conditions are right.

Naturally, for a healthy hoof to grow it requires the 'holy trinity' we have already discussed: nutrition, exercise and environment. For a hoof to be able to adapt and respond it also needs to be unshod, since a shoe not only restricts expansion, contraction and wear, but also limits the hoof's proprioception (the body's ability to sense where it is). Proprioception is required for the hoof to respond and adapt, and to balance the feedback from the surfaces it is travelling over with the requirements of the limb above.

Hooves can be perfected, strengthened, repaired and rehabilitated, or impaired, damaged, weakened and wasted. Much of this is under our control – certainly much more than you would imagine if you thought that hoof health was mostly determined by genetics.

These photos are of the same hoof four months apart: at the top lame and just out of shoes, and below sound and back in work (and not trimmed), though his hoof improved further over subsequent years.

I have written before about a recurring theme that hooves don't need to look pretty to function brilliantly. This is intimately connected with static and dynamic assessment of hooves, and it is why the dynamic assessment is so important – because hooves can look fine but may not be loading fine, or can look ugly but be loading perfectly.

You can imagine what happens if a foot which is actually in perfect dynamic balance is trimmed to a different, static balance: the result is often a less capable horse, and can sometimes be a lame horse.

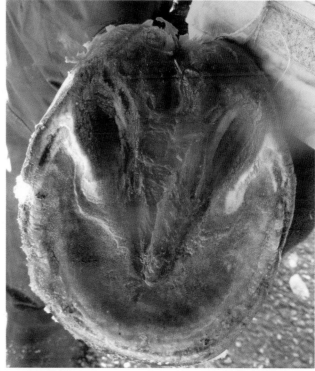

Hooves can strengthen and repair: these are the same hoof four months apart.

CHAPTER 3

Healthy Hooves: A Way of Life

Whereas it can be hard work rehabilitating hooves – bringing a horse with foot problems who has had long-term lameness back to soundness – it is in my experience far, far easier to keep a horse sound in hard work barefoot than it is to keep a horse sound in the same level of work in shoes. For instance, our own horses cover a lot of miles barefoot over Exmoor during the hunting season, and since 2004 all our horses have been barefoot. The combination of long seasons and tough terrain has taught us a huge amount about the capabilities of the hoof, particularly since all our horses were previously shod and several had come to us diagnosed with serious lameness.

KEEPING A HORSE SOUND IN HARD WORK

The majority of the other horses we see when we are out and about are shod, and it is common for owners to have problems with abscesses, mud fever and thrush due to the pervading wet.

Healthy hooves thrive on work.

It is equally common for shod hunters to suffer bruises from flints and stones, and they will almost invariably go lame if they lose shoes while hunting. Over a career lasting many seasons a proportion of the shod horses will also suffer chronic foot problems such as pedal osteitis, tendon and ligament damage or navicular problems.

Perhaps we have just been lucky, but although we have had a few injuries over the combined sixty or more seasons that our horses have hunted, they have tended to be one-off accidents: once a horse was badly kicked by a shod horse, and on another occasion a horse who was inexperienced fell from a steep path. Like most horse owners, we have had the occasional abscess as well, but in fourteen years, in a herd of (usually) four or five horses hunting once or twice a week over a nine-month season, these can be counted on the fingers of one hand. What our horses haven't suffered are any chronic, recurrent foot injuries or lameness – and this is despite the fact that three of them were originally written off with career-ending unsoundness.

My suspicion is that because hooves have to be very healthy to work hard without shoes they are also better able to resist injury. Good medio-lateral (side to side) and dorso-palmar (front to back) balance ensures that tendons and ligaments can function well and are under as little strain as possible when horses are working hard, thick soles give great protection on challenging terrain, and a well developed frog, heels and digital cushion allow for the best possible shock absorption at high speed and on hard ground.

HEALTHY HOOVES THRIVE ON WORK

It may seem counter-intuitive but, within reason, it actually becomes easier to keep a horse sound barefoot (in many cases unlike a shod horse) the more miles, and the harder the work the horse is doing. This is because healthy hooves thrive on work – and to be honest it isn't always easy in a domestic environment to give hooves the high mileage they crave for health. So ironically – given that barefoot is sometimes thought by the inexperienced to be a good choice for owners who love their horses but do very little with them – it is easier to find healthy hooves on a horse who is hunting, eventing, competing in endurance or hacking six days a week than it is to find them on a horse that spends most of his time in the field.

A horse can have perfectly adequate feet if he does very low mileage, but hooves being hooves, they will be adequate for what the horse is actually doing – in other words, very little. There is nothing wrong with a 'couch potato' horse having 'couch potato' hooves – after all, a retired companion animal needs nothing else, and will be perfectly happy like this – but really top class hooves will only get that way with hard work and mileage. So, if you want your barefoot horse to perform on tough terrain or in high level competition, or if you are planning plenty of long distance hacking, then the horse's hooves will need as much work as the rest of him before they are at their best.

CHAPTER 4

Tracks and Tradition:
Where Your Horse Lives

Obviously if you are working full time and don't get home until after dark for six months of the year, then giving your horse enough ridden or even in-hand work to maintain fitness is going to be a challenge – but there are things you can do to maximize your horse's mileage, and these are a good way to improve not only his hooves and overall fitness, but also his quality of life.

LIFESTYLE CHOICES

For a start, look at how long your horse spends in his box: ideally you want to keep times in the stable to an absolute minimum. This is hardly rocket science, as standing still in a confined space is never going to result in healthy hooves or better fitness, and to be honest there are so many other downsides for equine health – the increased risk of colic or azoturia, stiffness, respiratory problems, and the stress of isolation: so why would you want to keep a horse confined unless there were no other option?

Our own horses come into boxes for a short time twice a day when we give them their hard feed and check them over, but the rest of the time they can be in or out as they wish, and importantly, are able to be with the rest of the herd. They can move and socialize freely, and we reap the benefits in having horses who maintain fitness very easily, never 'pull out stiff' or have filled legs in the morning, and who seem to be relaxed and mentally well adjusted.

Unfortunately we have very wet weather at home – living on Exmoor means high rainfall, and as we are up on a hill, we very often have lots of wind to go with the rain. In my experience few horses enjoy this sort of weather, so it's important to give them adequate shelter. We use our barns, woodland and hedges to ensure the horses can always get out of bad weather, and also to provide them with comfortable, dry places to lie down – an essential which can sometimes be overlooked with track systems, but which is critical for health and welfare. If you are fortunate enough to live in a drier, warmer climate than we do, then you will find that the shelter you provide is appreciated much more by your horses on hot, sunny days than on wild winter ones – but it is still as necessary.

The key to keeping horses this way is that they can always make their own choices: they can be outside or in, at any time of the day or night and as they prefer, and they always have forage, shelter and companionship.

Many owners are reluctant to leave their horses out in bad weather, perhaps feeling that if they would rather be indoors themselves, then so would their horses – but you have to ask yourself whether your horse would remain standing in his stable if the door were left open.

Keeping horses this way means they can make their own choices.

In my experience very few horses would resist the urge to go exploring or to hang out with their friends, given the choice between freedom and solitary confinement.

On a stormy day our horses may spend most of their time under cover, but they are in a large area with companionship and a good supply of forage rather than being stabled alone, and if the weather changes they are free to go back out. If your horse currently spends a significant part of his time in a box, then it's worth considering whether there are other options available which could give him more choice, more freedom and more movement – all of which he will probably appreciate.

OPTIONS ON A LIVERY YARD

Setting up your yard and keeping your horses as you wish is relatively easy for those of us who keep our horses at home, but at the moment it can be much more difficult if you are on a traditional livery yard. I know many livery yards offer nothing beyond a stable and a patch of grass. For so many horses this means that life consists of time alone in a stable – often many hours – or time in a small field, which in the worst case scenario may also be alone, if individual turnout is required. I hope that as you read this book you will reconsider whether you can offer your horse a better lifestyle in a way that still suits you, and which doesn't require an enormous outlay of time or money.

Forage, shelter and companionship.

I appreciate it can be difficult when you keep your horse at livery, but it's amazing what you can achieve if you are a little creative and are prepared to at least ask about the options. After all, livery yards aren't in it for fun, they are in business. What that means, in the last analysis, is that they need to offer what owners (as a group) want.

When I was growing up, quite a long time ago, very few yards had a surfaced arena, and the only facilities you were likely to get were a stable, shared turnout, and if you were lucky, some space in the feed room. Nowadays many, probably most, yards have an arena, and many have indoor schools as well. This represents a considerable investment for the yard as a business, but over the years demand from owners has led to arenas being commonplace – and often viewed by owners as essential.

If we want better options in how we keep our horses we need to ask for them, and not take no for an answer. Changes won't happen overnight, but they won't happen at all unless we push for them. If that sounds harsh it is not intended to, but the reality is that we are responsible for how we keep our horses, and they can't lobby for what they need. Their health and happiness are in our hands. Since they can't speak for themselves it is up to us to speak for them and to be their advocate.

All horses are healthier, work better and are happier if their living conditions meet the needs they have – movement, companionship, and the basics of adequate forage, shelter and clean water. I don't think that is a lot to ask, and the reality is that if we set the right standards for our own horses we will encourage other owners to do the same.

So much that we view as 'normal' in the way we keep horses is nothing but. Horses have evolved over tens of millions of years, and for tens of millions of years they have roamed over wide areas, living in herds: they would travel for miles, and spend most of their days foraging for a tremendous variety of plant species. What do we view as 'normal'? In the eyes of so many it is to keep them in stables and small fields, often in solitary confinement, with restricted movement and limited, single species forage. But this isn't normality, it is just tradition – and it's a human tradition, not an equine one.

Then there are the various problems that we take for granted as being a routine part of keeping horses: horses going lame, horses suffering from colic or ulcers, and horses injuring themselves or us catastrophically when they strike into themselves or kick out.

Horses have only been domesticated by us for a few thousand years, and keeping them in the 'normal' way was developed even more recently – during the last couple of hundred years, which would equate to only a few seconds ago if you look at the whole evolutionary timeline of the horse.

The sorts of yard and stable that are commonplace today would be familiar to a visitor from the Victorian era, when horses were expected to work hard and had short lives. One hundred and fifty years ago it was common for horses to have a working life of four to six years, and in cities horses would be routinely kept tied in stalls when they were not working. There was no turnout available, and in any case it was convenient to keep horses in stables or stalls because in the days when they were the primary mode of transport it meant that they were always accessible and ready at a moment's notice, rather in the way that it is convenient to have your car parked outside your house.

There is nothing wrong in principle with a horse being accessible, of course, but our rationale for keeping horses has radically changed. Despite the fact that the reason for keeping horses is so different today, with most being kept for pleasure and sport, something is out of step because management systems have not always kept up with these changes. We have made improvements in welfare, and horses live longer as a result, but in some ways our management systems are broadly the same as those in Victorian times.

Nowadays, it seems to me, the way we keep our horses ought to be dictated firstly by their health and welfare, and only secondly by our convenience. I suspect that owners would not want it any other way, in an ideal world, but many livery yards are still set up to rely heavily

Horses are kept for pleasure, but our management systems have not kept up.

on individual stables, and seem to assume that owners still wish to keep their horses in a way that would be the last word in convenience and practicality in the eighteenth or nineteenth centuries – but which is less relevant when most horses are kept for leisure and competition, and worked for only a few hours each week.

TURNOUT NO MATTER WHAT THE WEATHER?

Two issues that are unavoidable in the UK are lack of space and the high price of land. The standard package offered by many livery yards of a stable and limited turnout is undoubtedly a function of the need to keep a fairly large number of horses in a relatively small area in order to make ends meet. However, lack of turnout and space for free exercise is often a major concern for owners – and it can be a cause of huge frustration for horses as well, especially in the winter when even less turnout tends to be available because of waterlogged fields.

This is a real problem in our increasingly wet winters, with flooding and prolonged rainfall likely just about anywhere in the country. During the recent winter of 2015–2016 there was an astonishing amount of rainfall up here on Exmoor: a neighbour with a rain gauge recorded rain every day from 3 November until the middle of February, with only one dry day during that period, and it was equally bad in many other parts of the country.

Most forecasters link this sort of extreme weather with climate change, and I recently heard a meteorological expert predicting that winters would become 50 per cent wetter during our lifetimes, so it is not a one-off phenomenon. Horses undoubtedly cause damage to land in wet weather, and in the sort of incessant rain that is becoming ever more common they will quickly destroy grazing on all but the most freely draining soil.

Tracks offer well-drained turnout in the winter.

Keeping horses stabled may not sound too bad if the alternative is a boggy field – after all, few horses enjoy being out in the pouring rain on sodden ground (which is often little more than mud) where they are short of grazing in any case. But with wet weather lasting for week after week and sometimes month after month, if the only alternative to turnout is being stabled for prolonged periods, then that is a poor choice, and one that can also compromise horse health and welfare.

Frequently the result is that horses who have been confined for many hours with no outlet for their energy because of bad weather are then turned out on deep, slippery ground, often with little grazing and no alternative forage. Predictably the energetic ones charge about making the ground even worse and sometimes risking injury, and the more delicate individuals stand miserably by the gate waiting to come in again – obviously thinking what's the point of moving around when there is no grazing and mud everywhere? – so don't even get the benefit of a bit of exercise.

It is too easy to say that more land should be available to prevent fields being poached and over-grazed, but land is expensive, and livery yards are often sited in areas where space is at a premium. They are in business, and under pressure like every other business, and more horses means more income, whereas buying land requires a huge capital outlay which is often simply not practical.

However, if the problem is that fields can't be used in the winter because of bad weather-because they are too poached to provide adequate grazing, you might assume that all would be well come the summer months. In fact another problem arises in spring and summer, often with these same fields, presenting a downside to turnout which at this time of the year becomes much more apparent: ironically, this problem lies in the grass itself. This is because along with our warm, wet winters come mild summers, and this provides a long growing season for grass, which also becomes very rich and sweet. This sounds as if it might be a benefit, but it is not necessarily so for our horses.

A life of eating sugary grass in a small area is not a recipe for good health if you have evolved as a browser and forager capable of travelling large distances. Just as we find it easy in modern life to eat too much and exercise too little, so do our horses. We have created a cushy life for them, and the combination of freely available sugar and inactivity is as bad for them as it is for us. Once again, the problem is exacerbated when space is tight, and once again the problem can be at its worst on livery yards where fields have to be intensively managed and are often artificially fertilized.

Highlighting the problems is the easy part, and the sort of armchair journalism which is critical about how most horses are kept is maddening to read if you are only too aware that your horse would prefer a better option, but all there is on offer is twelve hours a day in a stable and twelve hours in a tiny paddock, because that is all that the yards in your area have available. Even more frustrating, you are probably paying a considerable proportion of your monthly income to secure a place at this yard, even though you know it is not ideal.

SETTING UP A TRACK SYSTEM

You may even have heard of track systems and know they would be a better option, but like most people you assume that tracks are something you can only set up if you have your own land. However, in fact I think it is a system that more commercial yards should be looking at in earnest. We have had a succession of wet summers and wet winters, and it seems unlikely that our weather will dramatically improve, so we are going to have to make the best of it. This means that finding alternative solutions is a sensible long-term investment for anyone who is involved in keeping horses. Here's why I think tracks are a better deal for horses, owners and livery yards:

- A track is by far the most effective way to keep horses on a limited acreage, minimizing costs and keeping land in much better heart. It can make livery commercially viable even when space is extremely limited.
- A track is far more horse friendly than prolonged stabling as it ensures horses are able to move, reducing issues such as stiffness and filled legs as well as the risk of colic and respiratory problems. It is also easier to keep horses fit if they are constantly moving, and promotes healthy limbs and feet.
- On a track horses can live as a herd, which for almost all horses is preferable to solitary confinement and can help prevent or reduce so-called 'behavioural' problems (which generally equates to 'horses behaving normally but not conveniently').
- It is much easier to provide *ad lib* forage on a track, largely because when catering for several horses you can save time and energy by using bales and large feeders instead of nets or hay-bars. Horses that never run out of forage are less likely to suffer problems such as colic or ulcers, and are also less likely to gorge; it is interesting that a recent study on obese horses showed that they actually lost weight on ad lib forage, contrary to what you might expect.
- A track is the perfect way to offer grass-free turnout during periods of high risk for, say, laminitics (*see* below), and well drained turnout during wet weather. This means that fields are saved from poaching in the winter and can be used for a forage crop in the summer, rather than being sacrificed simply for grazing.

There are drawbacks to a track system, of course, but in my experience they are relatively minor compared with other ways of keeping horses, and for me, the health benefits for the horses certainly outweigh them. The first point is that you need to regularly poo-pick after horses on tracks – though this is no worse than mucking out while horses are stabled, nor should it be an issue for anyone who already poo-picks the field every day.

Horses can live as a herd.

The second drawback is that tracks designated for your road use will probably need to be surfaced. Although it is possible to make a very quick and cost-effective grass track in or around a field using electric fencing, this type of track will quickly become a bog in winter unless rainfall is very low or the soil is incredibly well draining. A grass track may also be a problem for horses with metabolic problems such as PPID (Cushings) or laminitis, especially as the grass on tracks will inevitably be grazed very short, and short, stressed grass is especially high in sugar – so this can sometimes be worse than letting horses have access to longer grass that is higher in fibre.

To give more year-round flexibility, the best option is to install an all-weather surface. First ensure that they are extremely well draining – it may be necessary to supply a membrane and hardcore in areas with high rainfall and poor drainage – and then lay a surface of 5–10mm shingle or chippings. This can be an expensive process on a large area of track, but it is possible to reduce costs by linking together existing surfaced areas – for example yards, storage areas or even unused parking space; this is how we started our tracks at Rockley.

The third factor that is often cited as a drawback is that horses mixing together will injure each other – though in reality, it shouldn't be a problem. We have used the tracks at Rockley for the last thirteen years, and in that time we have never had one of our own horses injure another one. This is despite some fairly crazy antics that we can frequently see out of the kitchen window, such as when the boys start one of their rearing games, or all the horses suddenly decide to charge from one end of the track to the other.

LIVING IN A HERD

Horses are socially skilful and are perfectly able to communicate effectively with each other; they are also adept at avoiding conflict, and despite some noisy body language there are rarely clashes. This is true at Rockley, even though we are continually introducing new horses and changing the herd dynamics, and it is even more true in an established herd. Occasionally a new horse is bitten or kicked by another new horse, but this happens only rarely, and again has never resulted in a significant injury.

Of course, interactions between horses are already much less risky if they do not have shoes on, and it is my inviolate rule never to turn horses out until their shoes have been taken off; I can appreciate that if you are introducing shod horses into a herd situation the risks are greater. Even so, I can't remember when I have ever seen one of our own herd actively try to kick another herd member; when horses know each other well, a glance or a laid-back ear is usually all that is needed to convey the message that someone needs more space or wants to be left alone.

New horses, particularly pushy ones, may well be on the receiving end of some filthy looks and a lifted leg or nip if they persist in overstepping the mark, but they quickly learn to respect the boundaries without the need for any escalation of behaviour. Having said that, there are always exceptions, and we did once have a Dutch warmblood who delighted in winding up the rest of the herd, and seemed never happier than when he was on the borderline of unacceptable behaviour and risking a serious telling-off from the other horses; but for us, he was the exception that proves the rule.

There is a fascinating piece of film of an experiment at the National Stud in Switzerland where a group of breeding stallions, normally kept separated, are turned out together for the first time (you can find it at http://m.youtube.com/watch?v=hAM5qMdOv8M). It is a master-

Horses are socially skilful and adept at avoiding conflict.

class in how much better horses are at effective dispute resolution than we are, and how much all horses, even stallions, benefit from life in a herd.

In a consistent herd of horses who all know each other it is unlikely that keeping them together on a track will result in conflict or injury (even if they are shod). Of course it is sensible to give bucket feeds separately, and to ensure that the track is big enough so that horses always have enough space to get away from each other.

I also treat the track as exclusively a horse area – if I want to feed, groom, ride, clip or handle a horse in any way then I will take him off the track and into the barn, rather than working with him on the track. This means I am not crowded by horses when I go on to the track, and they are not expecting anything, even attention, from me when I am there, which keeps everything very peaceful.

I'll be the first to admit that occasionally horses come to Rockley whose social skills are less than perfect, and the last thing I want is for a horse like this either to injure my own horses or to be injured himself as a result of his inappropriate behaviour. Nevertheless, no matter how ignorant a horse may appear to be initially, I have never had one that couldn't learn, and in most cases they are keen not to miss out on the benefits of herd life – and if the price they must pay for this is a little humility and learning better manners, well, that's a price most horses are willing to pay. A rude, bolshy horse will be excluded by the horses he wants to be friends with, so most 'rude' horses will rapidly modify their undesirable behaviour in order to be accepted by the new herd; usually it doesn't take more than a few days before he has integrated (or ingratiated) himself with the others, and soon it is possible to turn out even a horse like this with the whole group.

You do occasionally (though rarely) come across a genuinely solitary horse, but even for these horses track life is no hardship as they tend just to take themselves off and keep out of the way of the other horses.

Naturally there are occasions when a mare coming into season causes a certain amount of excitement, but again this is normally only a problem in a group of horses that are new to each other. Once a herd is established it is usually very calm, even when you have a mixed group of mares and geldings.

We are fortunate that two of our own horses are experts at assessing new horses and helping them to integrate without melodrama, and I rely heavily on them to ensure that such introductions are peaceful and incident free. They are masters at boosting the confidence of a nervous new arrival, or putting a cocky bossy-boots in his place, all without undue over-reaction.

If you are introducing a new horse to an established herd without the benefit of diplomats such as our two, then the best way to do it is to start the new horse off with one other, quiet horse, then gradually add the others one by one or in pairs. Setting up adjoining turnout can also help, so that horses can interact – meet, groom and sniff – but are separated while everyone gets to know each other.

With an established herd, life is usually very calm.

CHAPTER 5

How to Assess Dynamic Hoof Balance

The good news is that assessing dynamic balance is not a specialist skill. Over the years we have found that from observing very sound, tough horses with excellent feet – as well as horses with long-term lameness and serious injuries – patterns have emerged, which are repeated time and time again.

The soundest, fittest, hardest-working horses all have the same dynamic hoof balance when assessed on a flat, hard surface: a heel-first landing in all four feet, and in the front feet, medio-lateral balance, which allows both heels to load at the same time before the hoof breaks over at the toe (though the breakover may be off centre). This good dynamic balance in horses is a remarkably accurate predictor of soundness – in other words, you see this balance consistently in sound horses. Equally consistently, its absence – signified by a toe-first landing or a lateral-first landing – is a good predictor of current or impending lameness.

Importantly and very usefully, magnetic resonance imaging (MRI), which has been performed on horses with diagnosed lameness, allows us to link the lack of a heel-first

Sound, hard-working horses all have a feet-first landing.

landing with deep digital flexor tendon or impar ligament damage, and the lack of good medio-lateral balance with collateral ligament damage. Equally importantly, dynamic balance can be assessed with a camera or even the naked eye, and does not need any specialist equipment.

There is a huge advantage in being able to monitor a horse's dynamic hoof balance so simply because it can be done on a regular basis – monthly, if necessary – by any horse owner, and yet it gives you very clear guidance as to whether the horse's movement is compromised or not, and whether the horse's soundness is stable, improving or deteriorating. It gives you clear and definitive information about your horse's hooves, and it is also very easy to do – anyone can assess their own horse. All you need is a flat, hard surface, a smartphone or camera, and a friend to walk the horse for you.

There are a few things to remember when you are carrying out an assessment: the camera needs to be roughly level with the horse's fetlock and kept as still as possible (though you don't need a tripod), and the horse should be in walk – there is no need to trot. The surface also needs to be level; it is also pointless filming in an arena or on grass where the foot is partially obscured, as you need to see how the foot is actually touching down.

In order to assess dorso-palmar balance (whether the horse is landing heel first) you need to film with the horse walking past at ninety degrees to the camera; to assess medio-lateral balance (whether both heels in the front feet are loaded at the same time), film with the horse walking towards the camera head on. Be aware that it is normal for hind feet to load slightly laterally first.

If you are new to viewing this sort of footage it can help to film in slow motion (there are many apps for this), but as you become more practised you will be able to spot a good or bad landing with the naked eye. It is useful to view many different horses, particularly those with very good or very bad landings, so you develop an eye for what you are seeing.

This is the sort of footage that we use to assess horses on arrival at Rockley Farm; we then repeat it at regular intervals to monitor how they are progressing.

DORSO-PALMAR BALANCE: HEEL-FIRST LANDING

Filming a horse in walk can therefore give us a clear indication as to whether his foot has good dynamic balance: a heel-first landing in walk on a flat, hard surface indicates that externally the horse is comfortable loading the palmar hoof and has a robust frog and digital cushion. Importantly it also shows us that the horse is able to land and extend without putting undue stress on his deep digital flexor tendon or navicular bone, because a toe-first landing does the opposite. A basic understanding of anatomy confirms this – if you are interested in the detail then have a look at the following blog post, which gives the specifics:

http://www.rockleyfarm.blogspot.co.uk/2011/10/comparing-heel-first-and-toe-first.html

It is important to assess horses on a flat surface because horses will naturally land differently when walking up or down slopes: going uphill many will land with the foot flat or toe first, and going downhill a heel-first landing becomes more pronounced.

Incidentally, this is the reason why horses with palmar hoof problems frequently trip on the flat or shorten up going downhill. When a horse goes downhill he has to engage the heel, but of course with palmar hoof pain he will be reluctant to do this, and will slow down in order to put as little pressure as possible on that area of the hoof. Similarly he will be more prone to

A toe-first and a heel-first landing. The toe-first horse had been diagnosed on MRI with deep flexor tendon damage.

tripping as he tries to take weight off the back of the foot, or even lands toe first. This is why owners often report that the first problem they noticed, way before any lameness was apparent, was the horse tripping or shortening his stride downhill.

Over the years many horses that have come to us for rehabilitation have had MRI to diagnose the injuries within their feet, and we have been able to piece together how different types of injury affect a horse's movement. Most horses with what would historically have been called a 'navicular' diagnosis in fact have soft tissue damage – most often to the deep digital flexor tendon, but commonly also to impar ligaments and to the navicular bursa. If it persists over a long period of time this damage can lead to navicular bone changes that are visible on x-ray – the 'navicular syndrome' or 'navicular disease' with which we are all familiar from years ago.

Vets have long known that damage like this will block to the back of the foot – in other words, if a palmar digital nerve block is used, the horse will become significantly sounder as pain from the area is reduced or removed. You will therefore not be surprised to know that horses with this type of damage will typically show a flat or toe-first rather than a heel-first landing when filmed walking on a hard, level surface.

It's always an exciting moment during a horse's rehabilitation when he develops a heel-first landing, and it is an essential first step in his journey towards a healthier hoof. In fact I can only recall three rehab horses that never developed a heel-first landing, and unfortunately for each of these horses rehab was not successful.

MEDIO-LATERAL BALANCE

We can also assess the medio-lateral balance of the horse in walk on film. As with a toe-first landing, a horse landing with poor medio-lateral balance in front (in other words where he is loading one heel on landing rather than engaging both evenly) is stressing the collateral ligaments with each step.

A horse that loads the lateral heel only fractionally before the medial heel will be doing himself no harm – to the naked eye this horse will be landing evenly on both heels.

By contrast a horse that has been diagnosed on MRI with collateral ligament damage to either the coffin bone or the navicular bone (such as the horse in the photo on the left) will land markedly on the lateral heel and then almost collapse on to the medial side;

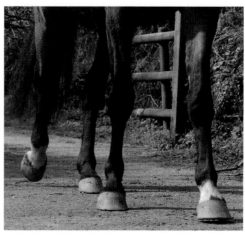

Landing laterally in front (left) and landing evenly in front (right).

this will be very clear in a still or in a slow-motion image, as the foot will tilt sideways on landing.

Again, filming the horse in walk is an effective and simple way to assess whether hoof balance and related injuries are improving or not. Medio-lateral balance can only be realistically assessed on the flat because obviously camber will affect landings, but it is on uneven ground that medio-lateral balance is really tested.

An important and fascinating aspect of medio-lateral balance is that it is perfectly possible to have a horse with apparently asymmetric hooves which nevertheless allow him excellent medio-lateral balance. The hooves appear, on a static assessment, to be out of balance, but once the horse moves, the way the hooves land and load shows good dynamic balance. Thus balance is not the same as symmetry, in that a balanced hoof will rarely be a perfectly symmetrical hoof.

Another important aspect of medio-lateral balance is how sensitive it is to interference from trimmers and farriers. Thus if a horse with balanced but asymmetric hooves is trimmed by someone who puts the hooves' static balance (how it looks) above dynamic balance (how it functions), then the result can be disaster. Sadly I speak as someone who has not only had to learn from past mistakes, but has also seen the mistakes made by farriers and trimmers.

IN SUMMARY

Most hoof and farriery textbooks focus on static, not dynamic balance, and judge hooves from a static viewpoint. Of course there are honourable exceptions, and I know of excellent farriers and trimmers who don't let themselves be distracted by appearance or symmetry if the movement is correct. However, more often than not, hoof balance is assessed by observing the static hoof, and in the case of horses with a functional asymmetry this can lead to trimming that is unnecessary, and which can even result in unsoundness.

It is, to my mind, critically important that we focus more on the dynamic hoof and become less distracted by the aesthetics of the hoof's appearance, because it is dynamic balance, not appearance, that is crucial for soundness.

CHAPTER 6

Rehabilitation, Exercise and Movement

One of the questions I am most often asked is what work a horse should be doing during rehabilitation. An email will ask me whether a horse should be hand-walked after a particular lameness diagnosis, whether they should have limited work when they first come out of shoes, or what sort of work level will give them the healthiest feet. The frustrating but true answer is that it depends.

Owners of horses that have been to Rockley are familiar with me saying 'only good movement is good movement'. What this means is that although horses are designed to move, and healthy horses will thrive on a high mileage workload, it's also possible to make a horse a lot worse with the wrong kind of work – so it's never just a case of racking up the miles and hoping for the best. This is true of any horse, whether sound or lame, and no matter what their age or overall fitness.

Years ago I was at a yard belonging to a friend who competed and brought on eventers. Her best horse was fit, looked well and was apparently sound. Certainly he had been competing successfully at intermediate level during the season, but she had noticed him becoming less confident on hard ground, and he had had a couple of uncharacteristic refusals.

In fact when we walked him up on a flat, hard surface the horse was landing toe first. For me this type of landing is always a warning sign of a palmar hoof problem because it is so

Landing heel first in front.

much more comfortable for a healthy horse to land heel first: to land toe first is awkward, a compromise, and means he has to shorten his stride, so it is invariably an indicator of pain in the back of the foot.

Engaging the back of the foot is a vital part of the normal stride phase for the horse. After all, the back of the foot is where the key shock-absorbing structures of the hoof are found – the frog and digital cushion – and so it should come as no surprise that using these structures and landing heel first protects the limb from concussion. In addition, a horse cannot fully extend his front limbs unless he lands heel first, and a toe-first landing also puts strain on the deep flexor tendon and navicular area. A toe-first landing is the first warning sign for a host of problems, and is a precursor of soft tissue (and eventually bone) damage and compromised movement unless it is corrected.

Improving poor hoof balance allows injuries to heal.

THE EFFECTS OF POOR MOVEMENT

Poor movement leads to worse movement as surely as good movement leads to better, so it is vital to have a basis of good movement before you ask the horse for harder work. If this eventer had been my own horse I would have wanted to improve the strength of his palmar hoof to enable him to land heel first before he was asked to work on hard surfaces, and certainly before he was brought back into full work, jumping and competing.

However, because he was not showing overt lameness, his normal work programme continued that season. Sure enough, over the next few months his performance deteriorated, and as his biomechanics worsened and the palmar hoof pain progressed, he did indeed become clinically lame.

It's a pattern I see repeated among the horses that come for rehab – none are moving at their best, and poor movement not only aggravates injuries that have already happened, but also predisposes a horse to further injury, poor movement begetting worse movement as the vicious circle continues. This is not even confined to the horse's stride length or levelness, as front foot pain also tends to make horses shorten their stride and hollow their back, which in turn predisposes them to back and neck pain.

Naturally, just as the feet affect the horse's posture, what happens further up the body can affect the feet. So if you put a saddle that pinches or constricts the shoulder on a horse with good dynamic foot balance, he will also hollow his outline and shorten his stride. And over time he may begin to land toe first and lose his good foot balance.

In the case of a horse with impaired hoof balance, whether dorso-palmar or medio-lateral, increasing exercise before this is resolved is counter-productive and can lead to further injury.

BREAKING THE CYCLE

We've established that a horse with poor foot balance risks injury from increased work, so what is the best way forwards? Very often limited movement or even box rest is recommended, but the problem here is that although it allows the existing injury to heal, if the underlying cause of the lameness – in this case the hoof imbalance – has not been addressed, further injury will tend to occur once the horse comes back into work. If weak hooves are a contributory factor in the hoof imbalance, as is often the case, limiting movement also reduces stimulus to the hooves, making it difficult for them to strengthen or improve.

A horse like my friend's eventer, for example, who is landing toe first, should not be worked on hard surfaces because a toe-first landing will increase stress on the deep flexor tendon. This is only a small aggravation with each step, but the faster the work and the harder the ground, the more significant the risk of injury. This is probably why so many horses that have had a mild, niggling, intermittent lameness for a period of months suddenly get much worse after a strenuous cross-country round, or following an unusually fast or long ride.

Rehabilitating poor foot balance always has the same aim: to allow existing injuries to heal without further aggravation, and to improve the weak structures of the foot to ensure better hoof balance in the future. This cannot be done without movement, but it has to be 'good movement' – so practically, what does this involve?

A horse with a toe-first landing always has a weak palmar hoof – the one is a symptom of the other. By strengthening the palmar hoof we can give the horse more support and help to make a heel-first landing comfortable. A heel-first landing reduces stress on the deep flexor tendon and improves the structures in the palmar hoof, leading to a 'virtuous circle': this is

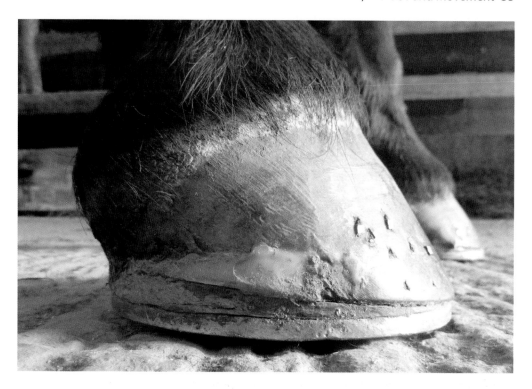

Remedial farriery aims to support the palmar hoof.

because not only can a heel-first landing, when established, protect the deep flexor tendon and navicular area from further damage, it can also continually stimulate and reinforce the frog and digital cushion.

Interestingly, using a remedial shoe on a horse with palmar hoof pain has the same objective: to provide support for the weak back of the hoof and encourage a better landing. But it achieves this in rather the same way that scaffolding supports a weak building – by shoring it up from the outside. That's all right as far as it goes, but a foot supported by scaffolding learns to rely on the scaffolding and becomes weaker instead of stronger. As a result palmar hoof pain, treated conventionally, has traditionally been viewed as a degenerative condition that will only get worse over the horse's lifetime.

By contrast, rehabilitating a weak palmar hoof without a shoe – done properly – encourages the whole foot to develop and strengthen. It has to be done carefully, and is not a quick process: it will normally take up to three months to bring a horse back into work, and it will be at least six months before he has grown a full hoof capsule that is better balanced.

The golden rule of rehabilitation is that the horse must move, but he must move within his comfort zone and in a way that allows the foot to develop better dynamic hoof balance – and for this, a heel-first landing is the essential pre-requisite.

ENCOURAGING BETTER BALANCE

Helping a horse with poor dynamic hoof balance to grow better balanced hooves can be tricky. Using different surfaces is helpful, and allowing the horse to move without the use of analgesics such as bute is essential. Although none of us likes to see a horse in pain, the discomfort of poor foot balance is not usually serious enough to cause him distress. It is annoying and uncomfortable, but doesn't usually stop him from ambling about, eating or interacting with his companions.

While it is tempting to want to spare him even this level of discomfort, it is there for a reason, and especially with soft tissue injuries (which we know are commonly the result of poor hoof balance and the cause of most lameness in horses with palmar hoof pain), pain is the body's way of trying to prevent further damage. When bringing a horse back from injury we need him to be aware of the feedback – the discomfort – caused by poor movement, because it will in fact protect him: when the horse is at liberty it will help to prevent him from overdoing things, and when we are working with him we can observe what movement is comfortable and what is not, which gives us valuable feedback as to how his injuries are resolving, or otherwise.

Of course any lameness is a job for your vet, and nothing can replace veterinary diagnosis and expert investigation. Filming is useful, though, as an interim tool to monitor progress, either with a healthy horse whose work level is changing, or for a horse coming back from injury, who will benefit from careful supervision to ensure work strengthens rather than weakens him.

From the point of view of an owner or trainer, filming is by far the cheapest and most accessible way to monitor regularly a horse's movement and dynamic hoof balance. Most phones are capable of footage of good enough quality, especially if a slow motion app is used, to allow movement to be scrutinized in detail. It's something that can be done usefully and regularly with any horse, and should be done every few weeks with a horse that is recovering from injury. An assessment of dynamic hoof balance should also always be done before increasing the work of a horse which is coming back from injury.

GOOD HOOF BALANCE SUMMARIZED

- A horse with good dynamic hoof balance should be capable of working safely on a hard surface even straight out of shoes, provided you work within his comfort zone.
- A horse with a toe-first landing should not be worked on a hard surface, but should be kept and exercised on conformable ground, which minimizes the potential for damage of a toe-first landing, until he has developed at the very least a flat landing and preferably a heel-first landing.
- A horse with a heel-first landing but poor medio-lateral balance can be worked gently within his comfort zone – in walk, in straight lines – on a hard surface, and his balance monitored regularly for improvement over a two- to four-week period; trimming should be avoided during this time, and any trimming that compromises his medio-lateral balance should not, of course, be repeated.
- A horse that is showing sole sensitivity on hard or uneven ground should have his diet carefully checked, as sole sensitivity is frequently caused by a diet that is high in sugar and starch, or low in key minerals. If a horse does not improve after being on a good diet for at least six weeks then it is sensible to ask your vet to run blood tests to rule out PPID (Cushings). This used to be considered a disease found only in older horses, but it has in fact been diagnosed in horses as young as six years old. It is eminently treatable, and modern medicine can hugely improve the health and quality of life for these horses.

Healthy hooves should be capable of work on all surfaces.

THE GOLDEN RULES FOR 'GOOD MOVEMENT'

It is often said that what suits one horse will not suit another, and that every horse is different. There is truth in this, but there are also ways in which every horse is the same, and so there are golden rules that can usefully be applied to every horse.

If the horse is healthy and his feet have good dynamic balance, then movement will be both easy and beneficial for the horse. In fact I think we have in the past underestimated how essential movement is for the health and well-being of our horses, in the same way that doctors have only recently begun to realize how critical exercise is for human health.

Only good movement is good movement. A horse that is moving badly – for instance landing toe first – will be putting damaging stress on the limb; equally a horse who goes hollow when ridden and who is unable to lift his back will be shortening rather than extending his working life. Bad movement leads to the horse becoming less sound and more prone to injury the more he does, whereas good movement will actively promote healing and better health.

Taking a practical example, it used to be common for horses that had been diagnosed with navicular to be prescribed exercise on soft surfaces only. You would often hear owners saying that the horse coped with work as long as they avoided jumping, hard surfaces or trotting on the roads.

It is certainly the case that horses with 'navicular' injuries generally have a toe-first landing because the pain is in the palmar hoof. And it is certainly the case that a horse with a toe-first landing will risk damaging the deep digital flexor tendon as he lands, and that this strain will be exacerbated by high speeds and hard surfaces. While a horse is landing like this, limiting exercise and keeping to soft ground will reduce the strain and is a sensible course of action.

However, if you can help the horse to change his landing from toe first to heel first, then the strain on the tendon has a chance to heal, and both limb and tendon can function as

Movement is essential for health and well-being.

nature intended. Over time a better landing will allow existing damage to heal, and if the new patterns of better movement are maintained, then movement becomes beneficial. This also reduces strain as the horse returns to work, which protects against re-injury.

Although an injured but healed tendon will not be as elastic as one that has never had trauma, once healing is complete then most horses are able to return to their former work levels successfully, and there is no longer any need to avoid jumping, hard surfaces or fast work.

So what can we do to encourage horses to land heel first? It is essential that the horse is as comfortable as possible. Even leaving aside the question of ethics, a horse that is forced to work with a poor landing or when he is in pain will be tense and will tend to shorten his stride and hollow his outline – the exact opposite of good movement. He will also try to protect weak and painful parts of his body: in a 'navicular' horse this means he will not load the palmar hoof, but will continue to land toe first.

To allow healing and better patterns of movement to become established, you will need to find a surface on which your horse can move comfortably and which deforms when he lands. This will effectively soften the foot's landing, reducing the detrimental impact of a toe-first landing. For all practical purposes, landing on a deformable surface has a less toe-first effect, which reduces the stress on the deep flexor tendon.

Critically, a deformable surface will also provide stimulus to the back of the foot, promoting healing and better development of key structures in the palmar hoof, including the frog and digital cushion. Over time, this will allow the horse to begin to load the back of the foot rather than the toe, which leads to a heel-first landing.

A horse that can land correctly will start to rebuild the palmar hoof, and in turn this leads to a longer, more even stride, increased shock absorption, and greater freedom of the neck, shoulders and back as tension in these areas caused by bad posture and hoof pain is reduced.

Find a deformable surface that is comfortable for your horse.

CHAPTER 7

Trimming, Balance and Symmetry

As a rule, most people judge hooves by appearance first – which, incidentally, is why any cracks in a hoof are invariably the subject of intense interest and concern for owners and bystanders, even if they are actually superficial and cause no problems for the horse; while the horse's toe-first landing is often a matter of supreme indifference, even though it is this which will result in lameness in due course.

If you consult a typical farriery or veterinary textbook you will find that they usually describe the ideal hoof as being symmetrical, and very often a hoof will be shown with a line bisecting it, demonstrating that the medial and lateral halves of the hoof capsule should look similar. Some texts prescribe optimum angles, while others talk about correct axes, but in each case the focus is the same: to judge a hoof by how it looks.

It is interesting that this 'ideal' standard demands symmetry within the hoof capsule even though, as we saw earlier, a well balanced hoof on a sound horse is not necessarily a symmetrical hoof. Using symmetry as a standard immediately puts the focus on to the shape and appearance of the hoof (its static balance), rather than on how it functions when moving (its dynamic balance). This focus not only overlooks the most important aspect of the hoof (its function), but also fails to appreciate how appearance follows function, rather than the other way around.

In a horse with flawless conformation and no injuries it is fairly straightforward: a horse like this will have 'textbook' hooves. They will be at the bottom of straight legs, and will be nice and symmetrical. With most horses – the ones with less-than-ideal conformation or previous injuries – it's not always possible to predict from the outside what the hoof should look like in order to provide the support the hoof needs.

This is because the hoof is able to – and will – always try to optimize even loading and balance for the limb above. In the case of less-than-perfect conformation or injury, adjustments cannot be made in the limb, so will be made at the level of the hoof capsule, which is more plastic.

Contrasting symmetry in red, with balance in green.

For instance, the hoof capsule on this sound, hardworking horse is outlined with the green line. He is a horse with less than perfect limbs, but allowing his hoof capsule to be asymmetric enables the limb to load in a balanced way and reduces strain on soft tissue.

His 'ideal' symmetrical hoof is shown by the red line. You can see that quite a lot would need to be removed in order to achieve a symmetrical hoof. Achieving symmetry would destroy the balance the limb actually needs for soundness. We know this because when he had symmetrical hooves he regularly went lame with check ligament inflammation.

We can assess dynamic foot balance through filming quite easily, as I have already described, but envisioning what a balanced foot should really be like – and what it needs for perfect support – is harder.

For instance, you will often see a photo of a mismatched pair of hooves with the comment that the horse should not have one upright and one shallower foot. What most commentators fail to point out is that the mismatch in the feet is the result of current and previous uneven loading (the upright foot is usually the lamer one, which has been loaded less, although over time the horse may also become lame on the 'good' leg as it overloads), rather than being an inevitable aspect of the horse's conformation.

Of course the conformation of the horse is fixed, at least in the adult horse, and the traditional assumption has been that hooves are similarly immutable. According to the old textbooks, we can judge a hoof from how it looks in the same way that we can judge a horse's conformation, and a symmetrical hoof must be the same as a balanced hoof… if only life were that simple! In fact the hoof is the most dynamic and changeable part of the horse's limb, and, unlike conformation, changes rapidly in response to loading, diet and exercise.

The second difference is that with a hoof, unlike conformation, we have (also traditionally) given ourselves the right to try to improve its function by changing its appearance . After all, surely if we make an asymmetric hoof look more symmetric we will be improving its function as well as its appearance – won't we? The answer is emphatically no.

It is certainly the case that a horse with no injuries, and which is fit and well balanced, may well have symmetrical hooves (though this is not always the case). However, carving the outer hoof capsule into an externally symmetrical shape will not resolve the issues of an injured, unfit, unbalanced horse.

The reason is obvious when you consider that optimum hoof balance is determined by the position of bones, tendons, ligaments and nerves within the hoof capsule, and by the health or otherwise of the frog and digital cushion. Trimming, even the application of shoes, only affects the outermost part of the hoof wall at most, and if done improperly is far more likely to unbalance hooves and weaken structures than otherwise.

Simply imposing symmetry on a hoof externally without assessing what is happening internally is like looking for your glasses with a blindfold on. Even if you try to trim or shoe with the benefit of x-rays, that will not highlight the stresses or damage to soft tissue, which are the most common cause of long-term lameness; only MRI can show this, and MRI is not a practical option on a regular basis.

Despite this, we routinely interfere with horses' hooves in blissful ignorance, hoping for the best, and are sadly unsurprised when the horse is lame after shoeing or trimming, as often happens, or when a long-term lameness fails to improve with repeated interventions. Why do we accept this? My suspicion is that we mistake good form for good function. The reason that we view interference in hooves as normal is mostly – perhaps entirely – due to the fact that it is easy for us to 'improve' the appearance of hooves, and so we believe that we are in fact improving their function as well. We have grown so used to thinking that we know best about hooves that we have forgotten to step back and see if the horse knows better.

Hoof balance is not the same as symmetry.

Hoof balance is not the same as symmetry. This is an extremely important principle, but is often hard for us to grasp.

The shape of a dynamically balanced hoof (when the shape is determined by the horse rather than the human) is supportive, plastic and adaptive. The hoof is being continually programmed by the load and stimulus it receives to provide the support required for the optimal movement of the limb above, including, if necessary, compensating for injuries. In an adult horse, the hoof capsule is by far the most rapidly adaptable part of the limb, far more readily able to change in order to optimize load-bearing than the other structures of the leg.

In my experience many apparent deformations of the hoof capsule (like the hoof in the photo), which are often termed 'flare' and which many farriers and trimmers view as something troublesome that needs to be removed, are in fact supportive and essential for good dynamic hoof balance. This is easily proved when removal of the so-called 'flare' renders the horse less sound, and on film it becomes clear that the hoof is less able to load correctly after the flare has been trimmed.

To those used to considering hoof balance from the static rather than dynamic point of view this may sound counter-intuitive – indeed, the starting point for many farriers and trimmers would in the past have been to sculpt the hoof capsule to the 'ideal' proportions and hope that this would encourage the rest of the horse to become similarly more 'ideal'.

The problem in practice with this approach is two-fold: firstly that trimming a hoof basically consists of one action and one action only – removing hoof structure. Secondly, although trimming undoubtedly satisfies the human need to 'do something', removing hoof structure (even if this is apparent 'excess') is rarely what a compromised hoof needs (I am aware there are occasionally exceptions, but bear with me – I am talking about most horses, not all horses).

Farriers and trimmers may talk of balancing a foot, relieving bar pressure, or encouraging development, but no matter what verb is used, every trimming technique essentially involves rasping off or cutting off external hoof wall. You can't augment with a trim, you can only take away: that is the only option available when trimming.

In the final analysis it is like going to your doctor with a pain in your leg and being prescribed surgery no matter what. Surgery may well be the best option if the pain is due to a bone chip that needs to be removed, but it is less constructive if, say, you have an infection and actually only antibiotics will help you, or if you have a fracture that will only heal as the bone rebuilds and repairs.

Or imagine you have a problem with weak, brittle hair and go to the hairdresser asking for the problem to be solved (without the use of hair extensions or weaves!). All your hairdresser can do is cut hair. He or she can fiddle with the appearance, put on lotions and potions and do some styling, but you will inevitably come out of the salon with less hair, rather than more. The hairdresser can't make you grow more or healthier hair. The only way that will happen is if you sort out what is causing the problem – perhaps a change in diet is required.

TRIMMING WHEN NECESSARY

Trimming as a strategy for hoof improvement reminds me very much of the episode of Black-adder, set in Elizabethan times, where he goes to the doctor and is told that the remedy for any and all ailments is a course of leeches. As he remarks, 'I've never had anything that you doctors haven't tried to cure with leeches: a leech on my ear for earache; a leech on my bottom for constipation...'

Trimming is just like a course of leeches – fine if the hoof genuinely needs structure removing, but irrelevant or even unhelpful in any other scenario. But nine out of ten standard horse management books will say that horses' feet always need trimming, and that without human intervention terrible things will happen to them. After all, we have all seen those welfare photos of horrendously overgrown hooves curling up over the toe like Aladdin's slippers.

The reality is that shocking and dramatic cases like this are primarily the result of metabolic disease or untreated laminitis, rather than simply a lack of trimming. A healthy horse in consistent work will never grow hooves like that, even if he is never trimmed, and even a horse in no work will only develop that type of pathology if he is suffering a metabolic or nutritional disaster. Using my own horses as an example, none is routinely trimmed, and it is almost as rare for me to trim a horse that is with us for rehabilitation. I've done it in the past but they simply don't need it.

I would go further and say – and this will cause howls of fury from some farriers and trimmers, while others will nod and agree! – that I have never known a horse which has become less sound simply and solely because he has not been trimmed. A laminitic horse may well move better when the pressure on the damaged laminae is relieved, but his primary problem is laminitis, not long hooves, and if you are able to resolve the cause of the laminitis he will be even more thankful and will move far better than he ever did after a trim.

I vividly remember going to see an elderly laminitic pony many years ago. She had dramatically long toes and a severe lamellar wedge, but her owner had been able to move her off the rich grass that had caused the problem a few weeks before. I was supposed to trim her, but the pony did not want to be caught or trimmed, and despite her ugly feet she jumped a hedge and bank out of her yard and cantered off up the (very gravelly) track, as sound as you like and not in the least footsore. It was a fantastic example of how even grotesque, laminitic hooves can function surprisingly well, regardless of appearance, once the trigger for the laminitis is under control. If she had kept on cantering for long enough she would probably have self-trimmed her feet, but unfortunately we had to stop her before she got to the main road.

A horse kept only on soft ground may well have a longer hoof wall than a horse in regular work, but change the terrain he lives on, and the extra length will quickly wear away. It may look unattractive as it chips away but the horse won't feel any the worse for it.

THE ULTIMATE HOOF EXPERT

We love to think our horses depend on us for their hoof care, but more and more of us are finding that our horses are already experts in this – and more self-sufficient than we ever guessed – and that hooves self-maintain beautifully without the need for a rasp or knife near them if the right nutrition, exercise and environment are in place.

As I've said, I almost never trim the horses who come to me for rehab, and of my own horses, one has never been trimmed (he is now a rising five-year-old), and two more have not been trimmed for over eight years. One of my horses is occasionally trimmed – say, every four to six months – when she is not in consistent work, and it makes not a jot of difference, positive or negative, to her soundness when she is.

If we look more closely at the evolution of the hoof it is perhaps not surprising that horses do so well with minimal or no trimming given the opportunity. Hooves have, after all, evolved to allow the horse to cover a high mileage, and bare hooves are incredibly adaptive to the surfaces they find themselves working on. This means that a horse who is working hard and covering many miles over tough surfaces will have a very much higher hoof growth rate than a horse that is working mostly in a school or who spends most of his time in the field.

Our horses are already experts in hoof care.

However, take the field-kept horse and bring him back into work (barefoot, of course) and his feet will start to grow faster; after a few weeks of regular work his hooves will be producing as much growth as the high mileage horse. Take the high mileage horse and rough him off, and his hoof growth rate will slow until, once again, wear and growth are in balance.

It's a truism that domestic horses are asked to perform on surfaces that wild horses are not, not to mention that we expect them to do so under saddle, but roadwork, and even the weight of a rider, do not put undue demands on a healthy hoof, certainly not enough to outweigh a few millenia of evolutionary refinement.

This ability of the hoof to respond to wear and stimulus is the reason horses' hooves can be readily self-trimming, and is the secret to a self-maintaining hoof. Naturally, wear and growth are balanced so that the hooves are perfectly maintained for the mileage the horse is actually doing and the terrain he is moving over. This growth rate is responsive to the stimulus the foot is receiving twenty-four hours a day and wherever the horse is moving.

High mileage and a high growth rate means that the hoof can respond rapidly to the demands placed on it and optimize movement; this is the reason that the best hooves are seen on performance horses or horses that spend most of their time out and about.

A TRIMMED HOOF OR A SELF-MAINTAINING HOOF?

It's my observation that the cells in the epidermal layer of the hoof are capable of reproduction in response to stimulus. We know that the cells of the epidermal layer of human hands and feet reproduce in response to stimulus: in our hands and feet, skin will thicken, toughen and grow faster in response to pressure and wear, and it would be logical to expect the same sort of process to be happening in the epidermal layer of the hooves of our horses. This would explain the changes in growth that we see in hooves once they are unshod, and it is likely that it is this type of process which allows hooves to adapt so sensitively to the environment and exercise levels the horse is experiencing.

Now think about what happens when we come along and trim a horse. Instead of a gradual and steady stimulus from wear and ground pressure we instantly (and in some cases radically) remove hoof wall and at the same time alter the loading area and balance of the hoof. This is the case even if the trim only removes long hoof wall and bar; the effect will be much more aggressive if the foot is 're-balanced' or if, as sadly so many farriers and trimmers do, the sole and frog are trimmed as well.

In this situation the hoof will respond by increasing growth to counteract the change in hoof structure and the perceived excessive wear the hoof has suddenly been subjected to. Over a few weeks things will start to calm down again – but then, hey presto, it's time for another trim, and the whole cycle starts again.

If, on the other hand, we refrain from trimming and allow the hoof to find its own equilibrium – both in terms of its balance and in terms of its growth rate – then we will find it is relatively easy to have a totally self-trimming hoof with wear and growth in equilibrium, and one which, more importantly, is precisely the hoof the horse wants.

Frequently people assume that this type of self-trimming is only possible when horses are in hard work. In fact I have had brood mares and youngstock that are just as capable of having well-balanced self-trimming feet as any other horse. It's not even necessary for horses to be kept on varied surfaces to be self-trimming, though some time each day on a harder surface than grass is a help.

Hooves can adjust growth rates to cope with a heavy or light workload.

The truth is that hooves are so adaptable that provided you make changes slowly and consistently, and, crucially, provided the horse has a good diet, the hooves can adjust their growth rate to anything from a very heavy workload with lots of roadwork to ambling round in a field for most of the time.

It is likely that the human focus on trimming (which in some cases seems almost an obsession) in part arose from the management of shod horses, because when a horse is shod the hoof continues to grow (albeit more slowly than in a barefoot horse), but there is of course no possibility of the hoof wall wearing normally or naturally. With a shod horse, therefore, artificial removal of hoof wall will always be required before the next shoe can be put on.

A corollary of ongoing growth but no wear in a shod foot is that even a well fitting and well balanced shoe will, as the hoof grows over four to six weeks, be in a more under-run position, with changed balance, by the end of the shoeing cycle.

There is an interesting time-lapse clip posted by New Bolton Centre Farrier Service (https://www.facebook.com/pg/New-Bolton-Center-Farrier-Service-118767734894305/videos/?ref=page_internal) which clearly demonstrates the movement in the hoof capsule in a shod foot over several weeks.

We need to reassess the role of trimming with barefoot horses however, because not only is it often unnecessary, but if we insist on trimming a hoof that doesn't need a trim it is very easy to unbalance the hoof and stress tendons and ligaments. Over time this can easily be damaging to the horse. We can also, by regular trimming, force a horse into an artificial growth cycle where he throws out excessive growth to counter the apparent sudden 'wear' caused by a trim. If he were left alone he would not produce the excessive growth, so would no longer 'need' a trim a few weeks later.

TRIMMING GONE WRONG

The problem with trimming arises partly because it is something we can easily 'do' to hooves, and partly because of the very human desire to be indispensable to our horses. It is gratifying to think that they depend on us for healthy hooves, and that we are providing an essential service without which they might go lame.

If the only effect that trimming had were to make us feel good, it might not be so risky. However, not only do we find it hard to resist the compulsion to fiddle, but it is very easy to go too far with a trim – even a moderate, non-invasive trim.

Many of us remember the shocking cases of horses being lamed by aggressive 'Strasser' trimming, which rightly resulted some years ago in the trimmers and owners being prosecuted for animal cruelty. Although this put a stop to some of the worst hoof-care practices, it is possible – even easy – to find photos and case studies being proudly displayed today by trimmers and farriers (not just abroad but in the UK as well) which show drastically overtrimmed hooves, with frog, bars and even sole carved out. To me this shows a barbaric lack of care for the horse, a total disrespect for the hoof, an incredible arrogance in imposing our preconceptions on the horse, and a breathtaking ignorance of how hooves function.

In reality, and with the possible exception of some severely laminitic horses (and even these are often made worse rather than better with trimming), very few hooves benefit from the systematic removal of structure, and just because we can do it doesn't mean that we should. The onus is on us – every owner, farrier and trimmer – to get it right, because it is much easier to do harm than good with a trim, although we don't like to acknowledge this.

How many times have you heard of a horse being sore after a trim or a shoeing? I have lost count, but I don't think I have ever heard that the person responsible immediately held up their hands, said it was their mistake and promised never to do it again. There are probably a lot of farriers and trimmers, including myself in the days when I routinely trimmed, who would quietly admit they have on occasions done a bad job, and have made sure not to repeat it, which I suppose is better than nothing – but there are others who regularly and repeatedly make horses less comfortable and less sound and simply carry on doing it.

A poor trim can have an insidious effect even if the horse is not immediately sore. Again, I have lost count of the number of times I have had emails or calls from people who are puzzled by their horse's recent loss of performance. Once the usual culprits of forage and feed have been given the all clear, my next question is going to be 'when was your horse last trimmed?'. Almost invariably the last trim coincides with when the horse started to go less well, but the owner finds it hard to believe that the trim was the cause because the trimmer is 'such a patient, knowledgeable person', or because they 'only took off a tiny bit, just smoothed the walls'.

Sadly, even knowledgeable people make mistakes, and even taking off only a tiny bit can trigger a downturn in soundness. Of course, not every trim is going to have this effect, but once you've ruled out dietary issues as a reason for loss of performance, the trim is the next place to look. For sure, it's highly unlikely that your horse will come to any harm if he has a break from trimming for a month or two, and if he improves over that time then maybe it's worth reassessing how often he 'needs' the trimmer's help.

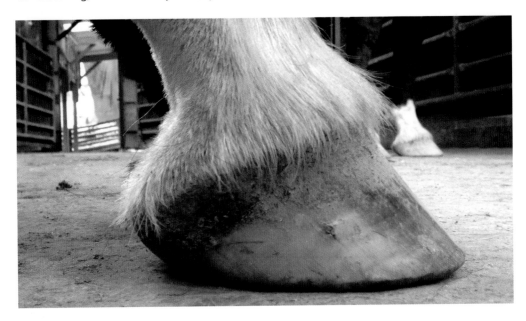

Few hooves benefit from the systematic removal of structure.

If you think about the structure of the hoof, there is only a tiny proportion of the hoof capsule which is amenable to trimming in any case: that is the hoof wall to the extent that it is proud of the sole, the toe to the extent that it is outside the white line, and I suppose the dorsal hoof wall, though dressing that is largely cosmetic. Go beyond this and you are into sensitive structures, and trimming those qualifies as surgery – so keep clear of these unless you are a vet, otherwise you are tempting prosecution and will certainly injure the horse.

Trimming, whether as a stand-alone procedure or in preparation for shoeing, is always going to affect only this small area of the hoof, and is the tip of the iceberg as far as hoof health is concerned.

The other problem with trimming and shoeing is that it directly affects – and usually reduces – the ground-bearing surface of the hoof, in other words the horse's loading area. This is why understanding dynamic hoof balance is an essential precursor to trimming: indeed, in many cases it should actually act as a preventative to trimming, for the simple reason that hardly any horses will benefit from a reduced loading area in the hoof.

Of course from time to time a horse will develop overgrown feet – usually a long hoof wall or bars – which can occur when a horse that has been in regular work on varied terrain is suddenly retired to softer ground. This can certainly look ugly, but it's rarely a problem for the horse, as it rarely alters the function or balance of the hoof significantly. Because the convention is often to focus on appearance and overlook function, it is hooves like these, which chip as soon as the horse goes back on to harder surfaces, that owners often worry about, though I've never seen a horse become lame as a result of chipped hooves.

Once again, our preoccupation with the cosmetic appearance of the feet means that we assume that hooves chipping is damaging, when in fact it doesn't bother the horse even remotely. Nearly always, this type of chipping is simply long outer hoof wall breaking off because it is proud of the sole, frog and heels, and it is being overloaded. On soft ground the outer hoof wall may grow long either because there is no abrasion from the terrain, or because the laminae have become weakened by the horse being on rich grass the whole time. This sort of hoof wall is not designed to support the weight of the horse, and so once the horse is on harder ground it chips off. This allows the horse to load its weight instead on to the frog, heels, sole and white line, with the outer hoof wall not taking weight but providing protection. The function of the hoof is unchanged, and in fact the chipping is a symptom of the hoof altering so that the foot loads the same way on hard ground as it was doing on soft ground.

There is some justification for trimming in this scenario, as removing long outer wall does not alter the loading of the foot. However, I tend not to trim even this nowadays, because I am weighing up the benefits of trimming against the disadvantages. The benefit is that the hoof looks tidier and the long hoof wall will not chip – but this is a benefit for the owner, and not really for the horse.

For me, in order to justify interfering in a hoof, I need to see a clear benefit for the horse – in other words, that he is sounder and more comfortable. The disadvantages of trimming are that the long hoof wall will be removed in one go, whereas left to his own devices the horse would have gradually changed his foot over several days on a tougher surface. This would have given his hoof, and especially the tendons and ligaments within the hoof capsule, a few days to adjust, which is almost always better than making a sudden change.

Another disadvantage of trimming is that the removal of the long hoof wall will most likely be done right round the hoof without being guided by wear patterns, which are unlikely to be obvious if the horse has only recently moved on to harder ground. Any adaptive support the horse requires for correct medio-lateral balance will therefore be removed along with the overgrown hoof wall, which may leave the horse at a further disadvantage, at least until the hoof grows back.

CAN TRIMMING SOLVE HOOF PROBLEMS?

There are lots of hoof problems out there – we are often told that 90 per cent of lameness is in the foot – and lameness is certainly one of the most common problems in the domestic horse. We, as responsible horse owners, want to do something to correct problem hooves if we can, especially the uglier features such as cracks, long toes and asymmetric hooves. So what do we do? Get them trimmed, of course, because what else can you do to improve a hoof? Of course if you want to go further you can shoe it as well. Frequently this is done without the horse improving as a result, or is even repeated, despite the horse getting worse.

Remedial shoes are frequently used by some vets and farriers – though not all, of course! – rather like some sort of medieval cure-all. You can picture the advert: 'The Bar Shoe, A Sovereign Remedie for All Foote Problems in the Horse.'

I have seen the bar shoe used for arthritis – though how will a metal shoe, which increases concussion, alleviate joint inflammation? I've seen it used for navicular, ostensibly in order to provide 'support' to the back of the foot – although the surface area of the foot is actually reduced, and the evidence is that over time the back of the foot deteriorates further. The bar shoe is used for side-bone and ringbone – is this because an unbalanced foot will be all the better with the horse's weight peripherally loaded? It's a favourite for laminitis (is it really a good idea to focus all the weight-bearing on the area where the laminae are inflamed?), and I have seen them used for pedal osteitis (increasing concussion and probably increasing stress-shielding, which is likely to weaken the bone still further). I've even seen a bar shoe prescribed as a cure for an over-reach (no, I have no idea as to the rationale for this, either). A course of leeches, anyone?

A bar shoe prescribed for palmar hoof support.

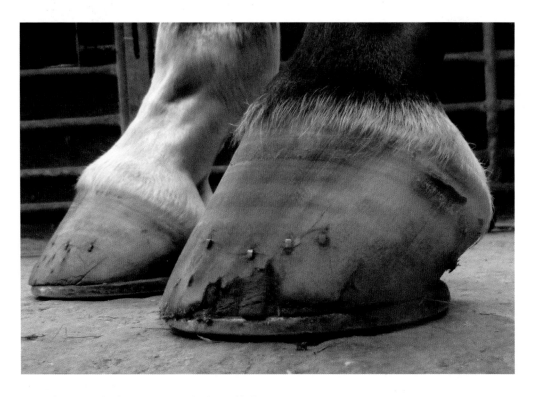

A bar shoe prescribed to improve medio-lateral balance.

Trimming (and shoeing) horses is a near constant affirmation of the principle that 'if all you have is a hammer, then everything looks like a nail'. It does at least tend to make owners (and vets, farriers and trimmers) feel better. After all, there are few things more frustrating when you have a lame horse than not being able to help him, and trimming and shoeing are at least 'doing something'.

Unconsciously I suspect it also, for every conscientious owner or equine professional, ticks the box that says that 'horses' feet must be trimmed or shod by a farrier every six weeks'. This is right next to the conviction that says 'horses that work on the roads need shoes' – though we seem more prepared to move on from the latter than the former, perhaps because the former feels more like a responsibility that we feel guilty about shirking.

The question that we should be asking, but which in fact is rarely asked before a horse is trimmed or shod, is 'what does this hoof need in order to work at its best – how can we enhance this horse's dynamic hoof balance?'. This, the most important question, can only be answered when we have seen the horse moving: it is not something we can discern just from photos or from assessing the standing horse.

Answered honestly, the response might be that he needs a less under-run heel, better qual-

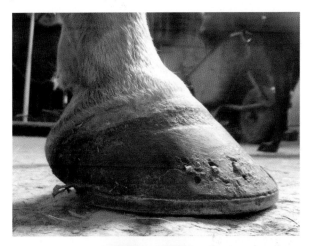

ity hoof wall, a healthier frog, more supportive heels, a thicker sole or stronger laminae – all of which are often areas where the domestic horse's feet could be improved. The shod hooves here are a good example – but the common denominator is, of course, that none of these improvements in hoof health are produced by a trim or even a shoe. Instead they are brought about by the usual suspects: better nutrition, a more active environment, and stimulating exercise. Once these are in place a healthier and more supportive hoof can develop and grow.

The feet in these photographs belong to a thoroughbred that had been shod young as she had gone lame. Despite this her lameness became steadily worse over a period of years. She also had a number of previous injuries, and rebuilding her feet was no easy task. Out of shoes, as you can see, she has become progressively stronger and sounder, and is now a credit to her dedicated owner. She is just one horse, but this is a story that is repeated time and again.

Feet on a young thoroughbred, shod, top and barefoot some months later.

It is true that in some cases a shoe can shore up a weak foot, rather like scaffolding on a building – but it can't make it stronger.

I know that my views will be considered as being anti trimming, even though all I am actually saying is that horses should not be trimmed if this reduces their soundness and comfort. However, even though a surprising number of people find this idea revolutionary (surely it isn't?), I am still passionately and unequivocally of the view that compromising soundness today for any trimming (or shoeing) agenda is counter-productive and unethical. My fellow hoof enthusiast, Steve Leigh, put it succinctly. When asked by an owner to trim her horse because she was worried about the look of his hooves, he assessed the horse's dynamic hoof balance. This was perfect and required no changes. She persisted in asking for the horse to be trimmed, and his reply was: 'I'm not going to lame your sound horse today so that you avoid a phantom lameness that you think might happen in the future.'

In other words, the horse knew better than the owner what his feet required. To my mind this makes complete sense, and it is more common than you might think.

WHEN AND HOW TO TRIM

I am not suggesting that your horse is never trimmed, even though most horses would be fine with this; however, it is a step too far for many owners at the moment. Instead I am suggesting that a trim is the least important thing you can do to help your horse have better feet. Since it is also the intervention with the highest risk of damage and the smallest chance of benefit, it's sensible to think long and hard before attempting to improve a foot with a trim. If we never allowed horses to be trimmed except where the trim demonstrably and categorically increased the functionality of the hoof, and if we only trimmed when there were equally demonstrable and indisputable benefits to the soundness of the horse, I think we would trim far less.

My experience suggests that not only would this benefit the horse in the vast majority of cases, but it would allow us to see the foot the horse really wants and needs, instead of imposing on the horse the hoof we think he ought to have. A fully supportive natural hoof is something which is rarely seen today, given that most hooves continually have an artificial shape imposed on them through regular trimming.

Without trimming, hooves can settle into self-maintaining growth.

This strategy would also get rid of the (common) scenario of horses being made sore as a consequence of being trimmed or shod, justified by the argument that 'he will be the better for it afterwards'. However, it makes no sense to think that a trim that lames a horse is going to improve its long-term soundness in any way, because a lame horse will straightaway move incorrectly. With this sort of trim you will therefore create precisely the soundness problem that the trim was (presumably) aiming to avoid.

By only trimming if, and to the extent that the trim demonstrably and categorically benefits the soundness of the horse and the functionality of the hoof, I believe we would also relegate trimming to where, in my view, it should be: very, very far down the list of useful therapies for most horses, and rarely, if ever, required for a horse in regular work. It is, at best, harmless.

ACHIEVING A SELF-TRIMMING HOOF

As soon as I raise the subject of horses' hooves being self-trimming I know I will immediately receive comments from people who say that it's all right for me, my horses are on a track and that's why they are self-trimming, whereas for them, on a livery yard or with a horse in light work, this is, of course, impossible.

All I can say is that I used to conscientiously trim every horse on the place, as well as horses on livery yards, and kept at home in hundreds of different geographical locations, every one with slightly different facilities and surfaces. I used to be as convinced as anyone else that what I was doing with rasp and nippers was really making a difference. Over the years I sometimes used to be frustrated that so many of the horses needed so little attention from me, but I still couldn't resist tinkering.

It was only when I stopped routinely trimming that I started to notice what I had been deliberately, but without conscious thought, erasing with each trim: the adaptations and asymmetries that the hooves were producing as and when they needed them. What was also noticeable was that, without the artificial stimulus of regular trimming, hooves were easily able to settle into a pattern of growth that was self-maintaining, neither too long nor too short, and perfectly balanced for the individual horse.

At first I assumed, along with everyone else, that horses had to be working or at least spend-ing time on tracks in order for self-trimming to be successful, but I tried the experiment with a mare and foal that were neither in work nor doing miles on the track, and their feet also self-trimmed.

Subsequently I have talked to a friend who keeps all her horses on a grass track, with no extra work and no special surfaces, and she has confirmed that all her horses' feet self-main-tain. The pattern was repeated as I tried to trim less and less, and even horses that did only light work, or in some cases no work at all, were still able to self-maintain.

Owners of rehab horses that generally do not need trimming while they are at Rockley also report that, on the whole, and even on livery yards, as long as the horse's exercise and routine are fairly consistent, hooves need little, if any, 'help' in the way of trimming. Understandably owners want a professional eye cast over their horses' hooves from time to time, but usually an assessment is all that is required, and horse and owner are then sent on their way, without any need for a trim, to carry on with what they were doing.

While many owners love the idea of a self-maintaining hoof, and are fascinated with the way hooves adapt once left to their own devices, there is a significant minority of owners who instantly respond negatively when they hear about horses that self-maintain their feet, with no need for a trim. They immediately state that it is 'impossible for *their* horse because…' – and the reasons they give are usually that they keep the horse at livery, they don't ride for enough miles, or (occasionally) their horse needs to be trimmed due to a conformation problem.

I am sure there are owners and horses for whom all these reasons are true, but what strikes me is that the owners who respond in this way are invariably absolutely convinced that they already have all the answers. They are sure that it won't work for them, even though they haven't actually tried leaving their horse's feet alone, because as soon as the hooves start to look a bit unusual they feel they have to intervene – very often they even say that their horse's hooves can't self-maintain because they grow too much and 'need a trim every four weeks', without wondering whether all that growth is actually caused by all that trimming.

In fact they are frequently exactly the same sort of people who used to tell me that there was no way barefoot would work for them or their horse – and on the whole they will give the same sorts of reasons for that being impossible as well. Now, it doesn't worry me in the slightest if someone wants to shoe or trim their horse. It would not be the choice I would make for any of my horses, but what you choose to do with your horse's feet is your own business. All I will say is that every reason I have heard is one that I would also have put forward in the past – *but* I was completely wrong, and never realized it until I started to listen to the *horses*, rather than to myself or the other 'experts'.

The fact remains that horses don't need to do a high mileage, or have a track system, or have perfect conformation in order to benefit from self-maintaining hooves or to go success-fully barefoot (I would actually argue that it's more likely to be the horses with conformational flaws who benefit from being able to set their own hoof balance). All I am attempting to do

The vast majority of horses can self-maintain their hooves.

is to make it a bit easier for anyone who would like to try it, and to reassure them that it is not impossible, and that, luckily for us, horses are cleverer with their hooves than anyone would ever have believed, and certainly know far more about hooves than we do.

What I've found over the years is that the vast majority of horses can self-maintain or self-trim their hooves even if they are in light work, or not in work at all (though of course it's better for the overall health of their hooves if they have to work a bit harder than this); also that it is possible for horses to self-maintain or self-trim in perfect hoof balance even if they have less-than-perfect conformation.

What you can't get away with, if you want your horse to have self-maintaining hooves, is feeding him a less-than-perfect diet. Hooves will self-maintain well enough on all sorts of terrain if there is a strong laminar connection, but once a horse has become laminitic, then self-trimming becomes much more difficult, and in some cases even impossible. Not only will a sore horse move less, but the hoof wall will tend to pull away from the weakened laminae, preventing normal wear and stimulus.

For a healthy horse on a good diet, though, self-maintaining hooves are a great option. It means you no longer need to rely on a farrier or trimmer to visit your horse every few weeks, but it doesn't necessarily mean you need to take sole responsibility for your horse's feet if, like many people, you either don't want to or don't feel sufficiently experienced.

A JOB FOR A PROFESSIONAL?

There are a few excellent hoofcare professionals (though sadly they are in the minority) who have a wealth of experience and can make a fantastic contribution to your horse's welfare. However, they are extremely rare, so if you have one, treasure them.

One of the key skills that I now look for in any farrier or trimmer is the ability to resist the urge to trim, and be aware of, and respect, the hoof balance that is optimal for the horse's own movement and conformation. The best hoofcare professionals in my experience will frequently leave rasp and knife in the truck and will expect to be paid for their time, knowledge and expertise, rather than for what they can hack off a hoof.

I think it's a real shame that the professionals who look after barefoot horses have been labelled as 'trimmers' – it goes back, of course, to the time when we all thought that a trim was really important, and that somehow horses could never manage to grow decent hooves without humans 'helpfully' removing pieces along the way. In fact, just as hooves require so much more than trimming for health, so the best hoofcare professionals will bring a whole lot more to the table than their trimming tools. We need to find a better term for them (preferably something a lot snappier than 'hoofcare professional') because the 'trimmers' who will do the best for your horse will do very little, if any, trimming.

What they will do is discuss your horse's nutrition with you, and help you resolve any glitches. They should be able to give you a range of options for mineral supplementation, and suggest hard feeds that are safe for hooves but also suit horses working at different levels and with different nutritional needs. They should be able to advise you on your horse's workload (I would expect that in most cases they will usually be telling you to do more rather than less!), and to make constructive suggestions as to whether there are sensible ways you can improve your horse's management. If you run into problems they should have the experience to suggest solutions that are practical and effective, and they should have the knowledge and training to be able to work collaboratively with other equine professionals, particularly your vet, when necessary.

It should go without saying, I hope, that any hoofcare professional worth the name must carry out a thorough critique of your horse's movement. Assessing your horse's dynamic hoof balance and how he loads his feet should be the number one priority, and they should be ready and willing to share that information with you and explain, if the horse has poor foot balance, how you can help your horse grow a well-balanced foot.

Personally I would only ever use a farrier or trimmer who has a large number of hardworking performance horses (working without shoes) on their books. Plenty of farriers (and trimmers) will say they 'do' a great many barefoot horses, but if the majority of the barefoot horses on their books are retired, youngstock or broodmares, your hoofcare professional will not have

Never assess hoof health from a photo!

enough experience to give you constructive advice on how to improve the hooves of your performance horse, and may well have no real experience of truly healthy hooves and how hard they can work.

Please never, ever, ever trust someone who assesses hooves from photos, and run screaming if they start to tell you how hooves should be trimmed after checking a couple of pictures online. I could show you dozens of feet that look very pretty in photos and yet the horse is lame; I could also show you lots of ugly feet on perfectly sound horses (as well as the ones in this book, there are plenty more on my blog if you are feeling curious). But without being able to view the horse moving and to assess dynamic hoof balance, hoof photos are just a curiosity.

THE DARK AND DANGEROUS SIDE OF TRIMMING

I said earlier that trimming is, at best, an innocuous pastime. For a long time I trimmed horses, some over many years, and I am fairly confident that I was (in the immortal phrase of Douglas Adams' *Hitch-hikers' Guide to the Galaxy*) 'mostly harmless'. Like any conscientious hoofcare professional, I walked and trotted up horses before and after they were trimmed, and made sure they were landing and moving at least as well after I had done my work. I sometimes thought and hoped that they might even be moving better, but I suspect that may have been wishful thinking on my part.

Over the years I have worked for some great owners, and together we became better and better at giving their horses the best diet and environment we possibly could. These horses had jobs they enjoyed, and even when it wasn't easy for owners to give their horses enough work over the winters, the longer we went on, the more the horses' feet became steadily self-maintaining; each time I saw them I did less and less to their hooves. Gradually I realized that these owners and horses had learnt all they needed, whether from me or elsewhere; they hadn't needed me to trim for a long time, and most no longer even needed advice or handholding.

The interesting thing to me was that if I had continued to actively trim the horses at every visit the whole cycle would probably have perpetuated itself. Horses that are trimmed every four to six weeks tend to 'need' trimming every four to six weeks, precisely (and often solely) because they *are* trimmed every four to six weeks. The hoof is trimmed, it responds by throwing out an artificial amount of growth, it appears too long, it is trimmed again...and so on, and so on.

I wasn't the first or the only person to observe this – in fact I think it was Bruce Armstrong, a fellow hoof enthusiast in Scotland, who made the point to me that, since hooves grow in response to the stimulus provided by increased mileage on rough terrain, we shouldn't really be surprised if they grow in response to a trim. This made perfect sense to me, and fitted with what I had seen in my clients' horses. By tapering off trimming over several months and intervening less and less but keeping work levels consistent, we had in most cases allowed hooves to become beautifully self-maintaining.

Hooves receive stimulus as they move, and respond by matching their growth to the mileage and surfaces they are travelling over. A horse doing miles on roads or on tough stony tracks will produce faster hoof growth than a horse whose life is predominantly spent in a field or an arena; similarly growth rates change as work levels reduce or increase, or hard surfaces are phased in or out. This is something we can all see in our own horses, and it had been apparent in my hardworking hunters for years, but I'm afraid I was very slow to put two and two together so it's just as well Bruce did it for me.

Roadwork, an easy way to achieve a self-maintaining hoof.

What this means in practice is that if you have a trimmer who always trims your horse, then it's likely the horse will not become self-maintaining because the trim interferes by artificially stimulating the hoof to produce more hoof wall than it needs for the work it is doing. In itself this may be harmless, and if your horse is always perfectly sound and you prefer him to be regularly trimmed, you can safely ignore this chapter.

If, on the other hand, you like the idea of having a self-trimming horse but are one of those people who (like the rest of us) thought that your horse would always need human help with his hooves, it might be worth slowly phasing out the trimming and seeing how your horse and his hooves adapt.

So far, so harmless – if trimming is benign, why am I so concerned about it, and so keen to make it a peripheral part of most horses' hoofcare? The short answer is that while trimming is, at best, harmless, at its worst it can reduce a horse's performance, weaken hooves, and even result in lameness.

Like most people, I used to believe that horses should be trimmed or shod every four to six weeks – it was simply one of the basic tenets of good horsemanship and something every conscientious owner should ensure: farrier booked without fail, horse's feet looked after, job done. In due course I realized that shoeing was neither a necessary nor a beneficial part of the process for my horses, but I still thought that the secret to barefoot success was 'proper' trimming and spent lots of time and money training to become a competent trimmer.

I trimmed my horses' feet regularly, as I thought that was the best way for them to grow better hooves. When I took the shoes off my own horses (as I described in *Feet First*), none of the trimmers or farriers with whom I studied made any mention of the importance of nutrition, even though I was taking advice from all the professional and amateur barefoot experts of the time, both in the US and the UK. It was all about the trim.

It's really quite shocking to think back and remember that, for a good year or so, I struggled in vain to improve the comfort levels of my most sensitive horse (perhaps some horses just can't cope without shoes, I thought) without realizing that 24/7 grass and inadequate levels of dietary magnesium were causing all the problems. This horse was being trimmed every four weeks, as was good practice at the time, and although she was no worse after a trim, it wasn't making her any better, either.

She didn't improve until I made some radical changes to her nutrition and management, at which point she very soon became 100 per cent sound, and has remained so ever since. Interestingly, our other horses who were kept on the same diet didn't need such micro-management, though many rehab horses since then have benefitted.

Even then (and this was back in 2004), the best and most humane trimmers were already aware of the dangers of over-trimming, and were adamant that horses should not be sore after a trim. This was an important step forwards, and is something that every hoofcare professional should still stand by – but sometimes I wonder how much progress has really been

Good nutrition is critical for hoof health.

made when I still hear of horses that are sore after a trim, or are routinely 'a bit off' for a few days after being shod.

Having seen how well horses respond when allowed to regulate their own hooves, I am certain that any horses that do – eventually – improve after this type of aggressive intervention have done so in spite of, rather than because of, the trimming. For me, this is one of those situations where there is no grey area: any intervention, whether shoeing or trimming, that leaves a horse less sound than he was previously, should not be repeated.

The damage can, however, be quite insidious, and many injuries that lead to lameness can be the result of damage caused by prolonged, low-level 'repetitive strain', rather than a one-off catastrophic accident; therefore it is possible for shoeing or trimming to slowly unbalance the foot, which over time leads to stresses that are not immediately obvious.

Charlie, ready to put some miles on those hooves.

I make no apology for including anecdotal evidence here, as a family motto is better to learn from the mistakes made by others, because then you don't have to make so many of your own.

Over the years as I trimmed horses less and less I realized that very often horses who were recovering from injuries grew feet that looked unexpectedly asymmetric. Usually this took the form of a medial wall deviation on the injured limb – an extension to the hoof wall between the toe and the quarter on a front foot that had suffered a collateral ligament injury, for instance, or on a hind leg that was suffering hock arthritis. With the benefit of MRI diagnosis, which many horses now have, it was often possible to predict which horses might develop these deviations, although this was never foolproof. It seemed logical to conclude that the deviations were supportive adaptations, and were either promoting healing or preventing further injury.

With hindsight I remembered that our horse Charlie (whom we had bought for meat money in 2005 as he was continually going lame despite being just backed and in very light work) had arrived in shoes, with check ligament injuries to both front limbs and with perfect, symmetrical hooves.

At the time of writing Charlie is hunting for his eleventh season, and has never since had a check ligament problem despite often hunting twice a week. It's probably no coincidence that he has also never since had symmetrical hooves. His feet are pictured at the beginning of Chapter 7, and it can be seen that he has a slight but obvious medial deviation on both front feet. With this he has fantastic dynamic hoof balance, with a clear heel-first landing and great medio-lateral balance.

My suspicion that hooves were able to provide adaptive support for injury in this way was confirmed when eight years ago I tried a disastrous trimming experiment on two of my own horses. As with so many disasters, it was done with the best of intentions, which is small comfort and no excuse.

An eminent remedial farrier was coming to see me to discuss the possibilities of carrying out research comparing growth rates and loading between the hooves on barefoot and shod horses (research that sadly never happened, for reasons unrelated to this story and not for lack of trying). I was frankly embarrassed by the appearance of the hooves on some of our horses, even though they were sound. I stupidly decided, against my gut instinct and better judgement, that the asymmetries in the hooves were just 'flare': purely cosmetic, and that if I trimmed the hooves into a more conventional shape the farrier would be impressed, the horses would never notice, and everything would carry on just the same. You will not be surprised to hear that I was completely wrong on all counts.

Following the trim the horses weren't crippled and looked fine walking over the concrete – even in my ignorance I knew enough not to trim aggressively, and all I had done was rasp a minute amount of medial hoof wall to make the hooves look slightly more symmetrical (you would have sworn not enough to make a difference) – I hadn't touched frogs, bars or sole. The problem came when the horses had to work on hard, uneven stony tracks: instead of being sure footed and rock-crunching as they had been before (on their wonky feet), they were tentative and footsore.

They looked so sensitive on tough ground that if I hadn't known that their diet was unchanged I would have sworn they had been given some high sugar feed. The hooves looked fine but I had made the classic mistake of putting static balance (appearance) ahead of dynamic balance (function). Removing the medial deviation had unbalanced the hooves and put strain on the collateral ligaments; the horses could cope with level ground, but on uneven ground the strain was increased, and it was this that was making them sensitive.

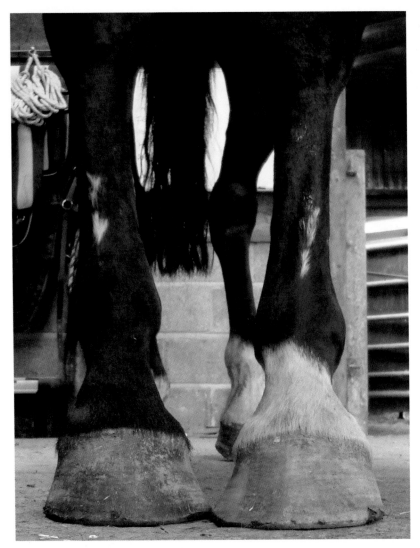

Asymmetry can sometimes be required for good medio-lateral balance.

Although it's a sorry tale I am glad to say that it does at least have a happy ending, because as the horses were allowed to regrow their essential hoof support, over the next few weeks they regained their previously rock-crunching status, and I, my lesson learned, vowed to be more respectful of asymmetry and to respect function over appearance in future.

This also highlights why a proper dynamic assessment of the hooves is so important. Both the horses I trimmed had good medio-lateral balance as long as they were allowed the medial hoof capsule deviation – a sure sign that removing it would be unhelpful. Nowadays I would always film a horse to check dynamic medio-lateral balance, and if a foot is landing and loading evenly with a medial deviation, then it should be left well alone.

It's no comfort that I am far from being the only person to have made this sort of mistake, as it is a story I have heard frequently repeated in subsequent years. Recently a horse that had been here for rehabilitation four years ago for a collateral ligament injury went lame at home. He had been a lovely success story up to that point, returning to competitive dressage and reaching a higher level than before his original lameness; he had even done well in his regional finals. He'd grown a medial deviation during rehabilitation and with this support his dynamic foot balance was good, as his ongoing soundness and improving dressage scores proved.

After four successful years it was a shock to everyone when he went lame. However, when his owner got in touch with me, she already had a suspicion of why things had gone wrong. In her email she wrote that a new farrier had spent several months 'enhancing' her horse's hooves and making them more symmetrical – but she had noticed that the horse was now landing on the lateral side of his foot rather than loading evenly.

Over time a medio-lateral imbalance had gradually developed, and eventually had led to a recurrence of his ligament strain. The end result was that the hooves looked picture perfect, but without his medial support the horse had gone lame with a soft tissue injury. Fortunately the damage was not irreversible and with a strict policy of controlled exercise and less human intervention on the trimming side the horse came back to soundness and competition again over the subsequent few months.

A dramatic medial deviation, which nevertheless functions well for this horse.

Although very few horses have perfectly symmetrical hooves, the dramatic medial deviations I have described are usually only seen in horses that have suffered injuries. Occasionally they will disappear once the injury has healed, but sometimes the deviation will be a long-term feature of the hoof. Even in their more extreme manifestations they do not lead to the horse interfering with himself, and in fact in every case I have seen they are responsible for enhancing foot balance and soundness rather than damaging them.

The bizarre-looking hoof in the photograph belongs to Dexter, a horse I have known for nearly ten years. His feet are a fascinating, albeit extreme, example of how hooves can compensate for past injuries to allow the hoof to load optimally. Dexter is an event horse who had been shod his whole working life; he was diagnosed with a DDFT injury within this hoof in 2007, when he was nine years old. Remedial shoeing did not help his lameness; neither did taking the shoes off and turning him away.

He was given only a 5 per cent chance of ever returning to work, and came to us for rehabilitation in 2008 as a last resort. He did very well over the next few months and came back into work; subsequent MRI showed that the DDFT injury had healed.

The extreme medial deviation on this limb is, I believe, the result of the previous soft tissue injury within the hoof. In the past I would have treated it as 'flare' and removed it, but when this is attempted his foot is unbalanced and no longer loads evenly. With the deviation in place, he lands heel first, has good medio-lateral balance, and most importantly remains sound.

Regular work is essential for him as it is the best way to maintain the health and strength of his palmar hoof. His feet are compromised, and are certainly not as robust as they would have been if he had never been shod and never been injured, but he does extremely well with the hooves he now has.

Since 2008 Dexter has not only carried on eventing, but he has also started a new career hunting and still competes in dressage and show-jumping as well. He is now in his late teens but is thriving, as you can see from the photo taken in 2016. He is a classic example of a horse who knew exactly what sort of feet he needed to give him the best possible chance of long-term soundness.

Dexter – the proof of the pudding. (Photo: Fiona Newboult)

CHAPTER 8

Building Better Hooves: From Bogs to Deserts to Tarmac

It is now a recognized truism that hooves adapt depending on the environment they live in. There has been research over the last few years into feral horses in various parts of the world, and the consensus is clear and unsurprising: hooves from an arid, desert environment will look different to hooves from a lush, temperate environment. For a while there was a tendency among some practitioners to hold up the hooves of desert mustangs as being optimal – perfect hooves to which all other hooves should aspire – but we now know that hooves are more complex and far more adaptable than that.

Feral hooves are often less than perfect (I am sure most of you are familiar with a predominantly laminitic herd that was studied in New Zealand), and can yield examples of tough, strong, capable feet or weak, compromised feet. However, the information gleaned from feral horse hooves is not always very useful unless we are working our own horses in exactly the same environment. As a British owner found out some years ago, Wyoming mustang hooves are great for Wyoming, but once you transport a mustang from there to the warm and wet British Isles, his feet will face the same challenges (including the risk of laminitis from high sugar forage) that any other UK horse would face; over several months his hooves will change accordingly, and even though he remains genetically a mustang, his feet won't look like 'mustang' feet.

Equally as another owner discovered when she moved her horse to southern Spain, if you transport a horse from the UK to a much drier environment, then his feet will become much more like desert hooves; you will also find that, in an arid environment with a predominantly

Feral ponies on Exmoor – a wet, cold environment.

hay-based diet, the likelihood of your horse becoming footy on too much grass is a thing of the past. In both cases all these changes will happen with no trimming required.

Thoroughbred hooves are another case in point. While they are often notorious for being weak and flat with a shelly hoof wall, I have known young thoroughbreds kept on a natural diet, given plenty of movement on varied terrain, and not shod at a young age who have fantastic, rock-crunching feet that can perform as well as any other breed.

Climate therefore plays a huge part in shaping our horses' feet, but it's also something over which we have no control. If you live in the UK you have to put up with high rainfall, mild weather and lots of grass, whereas if you live in Spain or Arizona you have to deal with extremes of both temperature and aridity, and grass isn't going to be an issue. In both areas, and everywhere in between, you can find excellent hooves, so it's clear that horses have evolved to deal with environmental diversity extremely well.

Of course, you can find weak hooves in most equine populations as well. Again, this can happen no matter what the climate, so what is the common denominator? It's really quite straightforward: what great hooves in every region, whether on feral or domestic horses, have in common is perfect nutrition and regular, consistent work on a variety of surfaces.

FIXING PROBLEM FEET

Many of the problems we encounter with our domestic horses' feet are directly attributable to historical management and feeding practices that weaken the feet. Traditionally, the best and fastest way to allow weak feet to perform as well as healthy feet was to shoe them. Shoeing was an effective quick fix and a means of dealing with the problems inadvertently created by nutritional deficiencies and poor management.

In the case of working horses a century or two ago, changing management or nutrition

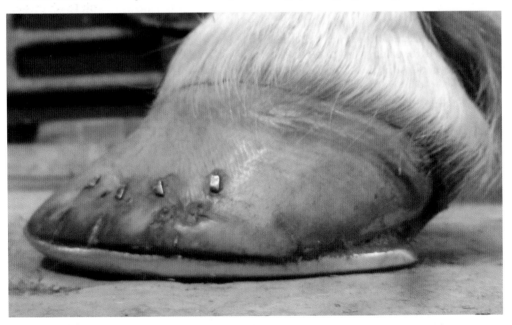

Shoes can sometimes allow a compromised hoof to perform.

would have been both impractical and impossible given the information and resources available at the time. Horses often had to be housed in stables or stalls, especially in cities, and their feed was dictated by what was available. Shoeing allowed a compromised hoof to nevertheless perform, certainly in the short to medium term, even though over a longer period it resulted in a host of new hoof problems.

Today we have many more options available to us. Shoeing is still popular, however, simply because nothing works as fast as a shoe in enabling a horse with compromised feet to instantly cover the same mileage as a horse with healthy feet. You can take a footsore horse, shoe him, and very often he can straightaway go out and cover miles on tough terrain. It might take several months of hard work to achieve this barefoot.

So often owners and equine professionals maintain that a horse 'needs shoes' to do a particular job, but I've never really seen a horse that 'needs' shoes. I've seen plenty of horses with thin soles who need either a better diet, or for someone to stop making the soles thin. I've seen plenty of horses with wasted palmar hooves who need to be allowed to develop them. I've seen some horses with compromised feet who need exercise and mileage to strengthen them. In each case it's not shoes the horse needs, but healthier, stronger feet.

When you have a horse with weak feet you have two choices if you want your horse to perform: compromise with a shoe, or optimize the health of his feet out of shoes.

In the absence of healthier, stronger feet, shoes may be used to enable the horse to outperform what his feet are really capable of, but shoes aren't solving the problem – at least not for the horse – though they may give the owner the required solution. Of course, there are many horses out there who have such severely compromised feet that they can never regain the health or strength they should have had. For these horses, shoes may well be the owners' preferred option, but having seen the incredible improvements that even older horses can make to their feet, often after many years of shoeing, I would never underestimate the horse's ability to heal. For instance, the horse in the next photo is also the horse that was lame in shoes on the previous page. He has been sound for some years now, and is a credit to his owner's excellent management of him.

Whether you are fortunate enough to have a horse with healthy feet and want him to stay that way throughout his whole life (perhaps you have a youngster that has never been shod), or whether you have a horse with compromised feet that you want to improve permanently rather than opting for a quick fix, the answer is the same. Although you won't get instant results and it may be hard work, optimizing your horse's diet, environment and exercise is going to give him much better prospects for long-term health and soundness than shoeing.

People who only have experience of horses with compromised hooves – the sort of horses who seem to 'need' shoes because they are footsore or short-striding without them – often assume that horses' feet are inherently weak as a result of domestication – but that isn't really the case. It's true that the way we keep horses and the work we ask them to perform isn't 'natural', but horses and their feet have evolved over millions of years. They have been domesticated for just a few thousand years so, in evolutionary terms, we have been tinkering with horses for only the blink of an eye.

Although there are many aspects of domesticity that can compromise horses and their hooves, usually the damage is neither inevitable nor (in many cases) irreversible. And despite the problems that domestication can trigger, with every year that passes there is better information and research available regarding nutrition, more horse-friendly feeds on the shelves, and people sharing innovative ideas about how to improve the management of our horses in a way that benefits the whole horse – including, of course, the feet.

An alternative to shoes is to permanently improve hoof health barefoot. (Photo: Amanda Stoddart-West)

HOOF HEALTH AS AN INDICATOR OF WHOLE-HORSE HEALTH

Working a horse barefoot gives you a great insight into the whole health of the horse, and this is, of course, an essential piece of information for owners. If you are fortunate enough, or have worked hard enough, to have a horse with truly healthy feet – feet that work hard over all terrain, day in, day out, and season after season – then you can be fairly confident that your horse is in good overall health because so many metabolic and biomechanical problems surface in the feet first. By contrast if your horse is footy, thin-soled, trips or is pottery, then you may be able to improve the symptoms with shoes but you are unlikely to have solved the underlying problem.

Steve Leigh, who at the time of writing looks after horses' hooves in the north-east of England, has a great analogy for what happens if you use shoes in this way. He says it's as if the oil warning light comes on when you are driving your car, but rather than get the oil leak fixed, you just take out the warning light. Your car would still go for a while and you might stop worrying (though even those who have limited understanding of most automotive faults would recognize this as ignorance being bliss), but the problem will only get worse over time, is bound to resurface, and in the end you either have to fix it or get a new car.

For what it is worth, my horse lorry is much more like a barefoot horse. When it developed a problem with its fuel injection not only did a warning light come on, but the whole system shut down into protective mode, which resulted in the lorry crawling along at a maximum of 20mph, and less on hills. It was incredibly frustrating but there was no question of ignoring the problem – fixing it became a top priority that could not be overlooked. In the same way, if you work a horse barefoot you will notice immediately if they become less comfortable on harsh terrain, and this should serve as an alarm bell that something in their diet has gone wrong – perhaps the spring grass is coming through, or your latest batch of haylage is not as good as it should be.

Faced with a slightly footsore horse, most of us will ask a more experienced friend or perhaps our vet or farrier what we should do; there is no doubt that we will receive advice, and it's also likely that there will be some in favour of shoes, even if there are also some in favour of barefoot.

There often seems to be nothing that horse people like better than sharing their opinions. Voice any query about riding, feeding, training, loading or keeping your horse, and you will find both real and virtual equestrians only too happy to give you the benefit of their expertise. Naturally all their opinions are based on their own experiences, and equally naturally many will be vehemently and sometimes even violently at odds with each other.

This is true of almost anything to do with horses – we can probably all recall debates on treed versus treeless saddles, rugging or not rugging and, heaven forbid, natural versus traditional training methods. However, as far as I know there is nothing quite like the barefoot versus shod argument for getting blood pressures raised and opinions outed – though fortunately as more and more owners have horses barefoot for all or part of the year there is a lot more tolerance and interest than there was even ten years ago.

Faced with well meaning but divergent advice – and often dire predictions of what will happen if you don't follow the advice – it is sometimes difficult to sift the sensible from the reactionary, especially when much of the advice on both sides sounds plausible but may be lacking in evidence. For example, I've heard numerous vets who have never seen a really healthy foot say that thoroughbreds can't go barefoot, and numerous competitors who have never jumped a barefoot horse say that horses 'can't cope' on a cross-country course without shoes; of course neither statement is true.

The horse is the expert on his own feet.

The best way, in my experience, is to bypass the 'experts' and go straight to the horses themselves. In the early days of working horses barefoot I was given a lot of advice, both in person and over the internet; often it was from people I respected, and even from people who had some experience of barefoot horses. I was told by different well-meaning people that horses can't hunt without shoes; that a horse's feet will wear away if he works on the roads; and that a horse will wear his heels away because his frogs are too big (yes, really – and this was a trimmer!).

However, my horse was telling me otherwise. He was full of energy and happy on all terrain, and was perfectly sound even after a day of hard work. In fact he was getting better and better the more he did.

The reality, with hindsight, was that the people who voiced their opinions just didn't have enough experience of working horses without shoes – they knew a little, but were extrapolating to the point where their advice was just guesswork and had no basis in reality. That didn't stop them having opinions, of course – they were only human – but it was my first lesson in listening to the horse rather than the human 'expert'.

DEVELOPING STRONGER HOOVES

You will also hear from plenty of horse owners who have tried to work their horses barefoot but without success, and of course this can be really frustrating for them. Usually when you look into the horse's management in more detail there is no great mystery, and you will find that the horse's hooves are not capable of the level of performance the owner is asking for because one or more of the elements needed for healthy hooves is missing. This may be

Healthy hooves have no problems with stony terrain.

something that is entirely outside the owner's control – perhaps the horse has a virus or a metabolic illness – or, more commonly, it is something the owner could remedy, but they haven't realized exactly what is causing the problem.

So, for instance, a young horse that has just been backed may be short striding or tentative on the roads or on tougher terrain. Traditionally the assumption would be that his feet 'can't cope', so he would be shod, which will probably give him a longer stride on hard ground, at least in the short term (this is a classic example of Steve's example of an oil warning light going on). However, if we look at this young horse more closely we may be able to see a number of factors conspiring to weaken his feet. Most youngsters are turned out all the time, and there is nothing wrong with that if the grass is 'safe'; but many are also brought into work in the spring, at precisely the time when sugar levels in grass are rising, something which can rapidly result in sole sensitivity, and may lead to the horse not being able to cope with hard ground.

In addition many youngsters will not have adequate levels of key minerals in their diet – many will be fed nothing but forage, or they are fed a balancer which does not give them good levels of the minerals that are essential for hoof health, or which is adequate in the winter but not in spring when grass sugar levels are high. Again, this can result in sole sensitivity, poor hoof growth and reduced performance.

Although there are plenty of mineral supplements on the shelf, there are at the time of writing only three suppliers whose products supply enough copper, selenium and zinc to make up the deficiencies that are commonly found in forage throughout the UK: these are Progressive Earth, Equinatural and Forageplus (none of the popular 'high street' brands supply these minerals in sufficient quantity). And even if you are using a supplement from one of these companies, additional magnesium and salt are almost certain to be required in spring and summer for optimum hoof health.

Finally, and equally crucially, young horses' feet have often experienced no surfaces more challenging than a field in their whole lives – a surface that does little to build a strong and robust hoof – but once backed, we expect them to work immediately on roads and rough tracks that are much more concussive, and without any period of adjustment or development for the feet. We wouldn't expect their bodies to be fully fit when they are backed, so why do we expect it of their feet?

If you are very lucky, then your youngster may be one of the fortunate few with great feet that need no special care – and a horse like this will cope despite the less-than-perfect conditions. More commonly, a young horse will be fine on easy surfaces, such as an arena or on grass, but will be shorter striding on hard, uneven ground, and may also be short striding on the roads.

For a young horse like this a shoe provides an instant fix (though it does nothing to lessen concussion), a way of enhancing the performance of the hoof far more rapidly than if you were to change his nutrition and steadily develop the strength of the foot by exercise on different surfaces.

Sometimes an instant fix is a useful option to fall back on, but we need to realize that – as with most quick fixes – there will be a down side, and most often this will be that the horse will continue to be shod, and that his hooves will at best not fully develop (particularly the palmar hoof), and at worst (though certainly not inevitably) will start to fail further down the line.

Years later some owners, faced with failing hooves, will then turn to barefoot as a last resort. This is often very worthwhile, but I would advise anyone who is thinking about working a horse without shoes to try it at an earlier stage, for the best results – optimizing rather than compromising the hooves.

I should make it clear, though, that in my experience problems arise not directly as a result of shoeing, but due to the knock-on effect of a weakened palmar hoof, and in the case of metabolic issues such as laminitis and PPID, the lack of an early warning in the health of the foot (as symptoms such as sole sensitivity are masked by shoes), both of which are common effects of long-term shoeing.

GOOD HOOVES FOR THE LONG TERM

In the end, whether the horse has shoes on or not, most lamenesses are caused because the horse's metabolism or biomechanics have been compromised. Nutrition and management issues are often implicated in metabolic problems, and ongoing poor foot balance is commonly associated with poor biomechanics. These factors can, of course, affect barefoot horses as well as shod ones, but from what I see here the horses that are already barefoot recover much more quickly than the shod horses. Although it's always upsetting for the owner when a horse is ill or injured, owners of barefoot horses have an easier time, on the whole, in dealing with setbacks such as this.

Firstly, it's far easier for the horse to maintain optimal foot balance out of shoes, particularly if human intervention is minimized. Secondly, an owner will almost always have much earlier warning of impending metabolic problems in a barefoot horse than in a shod horse, meaning damage can be minimized. Thirdly, a horse that has always been barefoot will tend to have a much thicker sole, a tougher frog and a more robust digital cushion than a shod horse, and this in itself can provide significant protection from injury.

Young horses enjoy life on the tracks just as much as older horses.

I would argue that the alternative, holistic approach of building a healthier hoof is not only more ethical and more sustainable, it is also likely to give longer-term soundness as well. Too often we forget that hooves, like the rest of the horse, can be either fit or unfit, weak or strong, and that hooves, like the rest of the body, are going through a constant process of rebuilding and improving, or failing and deteriorating, depending on their state of health.

We have always kept our youngsters on the same routine as the older horses, so they spend part of their time on tougher surfaces even when they are babies. They are also always fed the same mineral supplements as the adult horses; they may not be in work, but they have exactly the same need to grow healthy feet and be fed a properly balanced diet. We make time to take them out on the roads long before they will ever do ridden work. This gives their feet some exposure to hard ground, which helps build a robust frog, heel and digital cushion, and also gives them more mental stimulation and teaches them better manners than just being turned out in a field. We are fortunate enough to have quiet roads, and most seem to really enjoy going out with the 'big horses'.

I also feel instinctively that it is easier for them to have their education broken down into many small steps, rather than having to deal with traffic, ridden work and the big wide world all at the same time.

There is another factor at play with a young horse – something so obvious that with the rest of the horse it goes without saying. In other words, you don't expect a four-year-old horse to be fit and correctly muscled at the time he is backed (though he will be more so if he has done the sort of in-hand work I described above, before anyone ever sits on him). Realistically you would expect it to take months, and even years, of correct work before he is as strong and fit under saddle as he can be, and this is even truer if you are asking him for a high level of work.

A healthy hoof is exactly the same, and a typical four-year-old horse will not, when he begins work, have as strong and well developed a foot as the same horse after a year or two of solid mileage over all terrain. If he were a feral horse he would have covered many more miles in his first few years, but of course free-range high mileage is not a typical feature of life for the domestic horse.

It is possible for any horse, even one that has come out of shoes in his teens or twenties, to build a stronger foot, but it is particularly important for a young horse to be given the opportunity to do so. Of course, one possible explanation for racehorses having notoriously poor hooves is the effect that very early shoeing can have on the foot.

It is difficult to isolate the shoeing alone, as racehorses also tend to have a high sugar diet and restricted movement (these also have an adverse effect on many horses' hooves), so this can only be conjecture – but it's a common pattern. It also seems generally true that flat racehorses, which are shod younger as a rule than National Hunt horses, but otherwise kept in similar conditions, tend to have a weaker palmar hoof than National Hunt horses; it would be logical if this were the result of earlier shoeing.

By contrast I have come across a number of young thoroughbreds that have never raced and have been kept more sympathetically, with plenty of turnout and mileage, a low sugar, high fibre diet with good mineral supplementation, and which have not been shod until they are at least four years old, or are allowed to stay barefoot. These horses without exception have terrific feet, so there is obviously more at work than simply genetics.

It would be a fascinating experiment to take genetically similar thoroughbred foals and bring them up in different environments and with different hoofcare regimes, but I suspect the results would be a foregone conclusion.

CHAPTER 9

The Importance of Research

One of the criticisms regularly raised by vets, farriers and other horse owners is that there is little research to support barefoot as a therapy – especially when an owner proposes taking a horse barefoot as a way of improving a condition such as palmar hoof pain (a term used in this book to describe any lameness caused by navicular bone or bursa damage, deep flexor tendon damage or related impar or collateral ligament damage).

I have a huge amount of sympathy with this view – after all, we are all aware that 'miracle cures', backed up by suspect or downright spurious pseudo-science, are touted all over the internet and it is all too easy for barefoot to be classed as yet another illogical fad by non-believers. However, a number of factors should be considered before barefoot is dismissed for lack of supporting evidence.

Firstly, the problem of research being in short supply affects much more than just the bare-foot horse. Not only is there little research into the basic function of high-performing bare hooves, but evidence, and especially high quality research, is – contrary to what you might expect – lacking for many common veterinary therapies. As vet Becca Hart, whose own horses event barefoot, says:

Good quality research is not common in any area of veterinary medicine. If you want to make your vet very uncomfortable, ask them for the research backing up what they are doing and check the sample size and whether there is any control group. [Veterinary medicine] is still very much an art, with a bit of science and common sense thrown in.

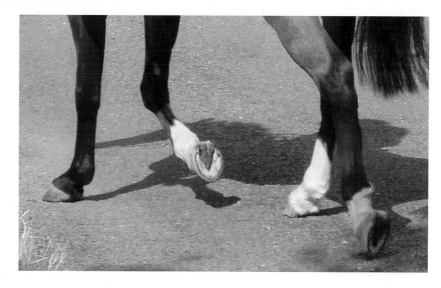

There is little research into the basic function of hooves.

The reality is that research grants for veterinary medicine are in short supply. While there is a tremendous appetite for new research in any number of areas, demand completely outstrips the available funding, meaning that vets are often forced to prescribe therapies without having extensive research to back them up.

Despite this less-than-ideal situation, most vets and owners are strongly supportive of veterinary medicine being evidence based. 'Evidence-based medicine' is a term that is widely used in the human medical world, describing best practice when deciding appropriate treatment options for patients. The term was coined to describe 'the conscientious, explicit and judicious use of current best evidence in making decisions.' ('Evidence based medicine: what it is and what it isn't' *British Medical Journal* 1996; 312:71).

From a purely selfish viewpoint, nothing would delight me more than a research programme that was dedicated to the barefoot horse – but we have to be realistic as well as scientific, so let's look at the facts.

Firstly, evidence-based medicine is only ever as good as the evidence that is actually available. This means that where evidence exists, there is a recognized hierarchy that ranks its quality, and indicates which types of evidence should be the most and the least influential.

This hierarchy is a pyramid which has the double-blind, randomized controlled study as the highest quality, 'gold standard' evidence, while down at the bottom are observations that form the lowest ranking type of evidence. In between are other sorts of evidence: the greater the sample numbers, the more rigorously they are verified and the more objective they are, the greater the importance that will be given to them. So individual case reports rank lower than a larger collection of reports, and case studies that include a control group are viewed as more authoritative still.

Evidence is vital in making treatment decisions, but in the real world the best available evidence also needs to be combined with the clinician's individual expertise, all the time ensuring that the patient's values and concerns are also taken into account.

In this three-way approach evidence plays an essential part, but one piece of evidence is not necessarily overwhelming. Critically, evidence may be available at any level of the pyramid, so if 'gold standard' randomized controlled studies are not available, then evidence from the lower levels assumes greater importance.

Much as we might prefer our vets only to use therapies that have been the subject of double-blind, randomized controlled trials, these trials are few and far between in the veterinary field, and as funding and resources continue to be tightly constrained there are unlikely to be extensive new trials any time soon.

Although that may sound limiting, in practical terms it means that we need to look carefully at all the available evidence. It is already the case that the value of smaller studies is recognized in human and veterinary medicine, especially for innovative new treatments that are at an experimental stage.

Next we need to recognize that the threshold for the evidence that is required in order to make a decision in favour of a treatment or therapy depends not only on how invasive it is and how serious the side effects could be, but also on what other treatments are available, and what the prognosis is without treatment – in other words, what alternative or better options are available, if any.

So for instance, it may well be an appropriate decision to try an experimental treatment that is risky or invasive when the patient otherwise has no hope of survival. Equally it may be acceptable to try a very safe, non-invasive but experimental treatment where there are no side effects, because the risks to the patient's welfare are minimal even if the treatment is ineffective.

A fascinating development in human medicine has been the assessment of therapies and interventions using the measurement 'number-needed-to-treat', or NNT (http://thennt.com). This framework evaluates therapies based on their benefits and harms to patients, and provides an incredible insight into the effectiveness of interventions over large numbers of people and long periods of time, which can give a broader perspective than traditional data alone.

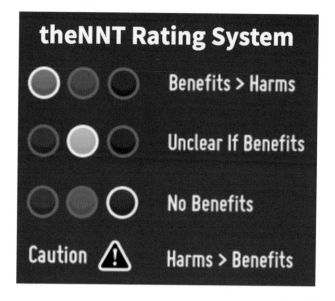

Following a review of the evidence, NNT rates therapies in a colour-coded scale: green is for those where clear benefits outweigh any associated harms; yellow is inconclusive, for therapies where more studies are needed;

The NNT system evaluates therapies.

red highlights therapies where benefits don't outweigh harms; and black, the worst rating, indicates therapies with clear harms and no associated benefits. A notable feature of NNT reviews is that they are independent: the reviewers are not funded by pharmaceutical companies or other industry bodies, and so their conclusions tend to be more objective.

One interesting example is a review of the evidence for statins, which have been widely prescribed as a means of reducing the risk of heart attacks even in patients who had not suffered an attack. On review, NNT concluded that although statins certainly reduce cholesterol, they did not reduce mortality from heart attacks: there were no fewer deaths in patients taking statins. In addition, although taking statins had benefits (preventing heart attacks in one in sixty people, and strokes in one in 268 people), these were outweighed by the harms caused by taking statins (one in fifty people developed diabetes, and one in ten had muscle damage).

So how is this relevant to horses and hooves? Simply because it provides a good illustration that even the best evidence can be skewed by conflicts of interest, and that just because we can intervene doesn't necessarily mean we should, particularly if benefits are apparent only in the short term, but significant harms may take longer to develop.

Incidentally, another NNT review found that following a Mediterranean diet could actually prevent heart attacks and stroke, and rated this as a 'green' therapy – one of the best. One in sixty-one patients benefitted through the prevention of a stroke, heart attack or death, and none was harmed, making it much more successful than statins. There are obvious similarities in this for what we see in hooves, where nutrition is absolutely critical for health.

When the first horses came to Rockley for rehabilitation we had little evidence, beyond the small numbers of our own horses that had come sound, that we could present to vets and owners. Despite this, those first owners found it easy to make the decision to send their horses to us (and their vets agreed), because all other treatment options had been exhausted, and in each case the horses would otherwise have been put down due to ongoing lameness.

Twenty years ago I actually believed that horses could not work on the roads without shoes.

A few years down the line we had seen larger numbers of horses and had collected data on them over the longer term, and so we were able to produce better quality evidence. This meant that owners could be more confident about sending horses that had been recently diagnosed, choosing rehabilitation rather than waiting until other treatments had failed.

Evidence is extremely helpful, of course, when you are faced with a horse that has become lame, but I would argue that the decision to take a horse barefoot is not actually a decision that requires an extensive evidence base in order to be acceptable. Horses are born without shoes, after all, so soundness barefoot is a condition that horses experience as the norm at the start of their lives.

Even where a horse has previously been shod, in most cases the worst that can happen if you take him barefoot is that he may be footsore immediately he comes out of shoes. This is always something which can (and should) be quickly alleviated, and there is nowadays a wealth of options available that can help keep horses comfortable in the initial stages of growing better hooves, from feed information to hoof boots.

As I have outlined earlier, the case for deciding to take a horse barefoot is even more compelling where the horse has been diagnosed with palmar hoof pain or a condition such as 'navicular disease', which is usually (though in my opinion wrongly) classed as degenerative, and where the prognosis with conventional treatments is guarded or poor. It is especially ironic when conventional treatments are applied, even though the assumption is that your horse will get worse no matter what is done. In fact, with proper rehabilitation out of shoes,

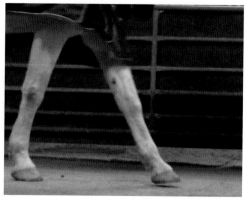

These photos show an eventer's improvement over twelve weeks of rehab.

and proper attention being paid to how the horse is landing and loading his feet, the evidence is that this type of lameness does not continue to degenerate over time.

Although the evidence to support my assertions is not the élite evidence of a randomized controlled trial, there is still plenty out there. It's not just evidence from the horses that have been with us here at Rockley, but from dozens and dozens, if not hundreds of other horses whose owners now send me photos of their 'written off' navicular horses, which they now proudly show hacking, jumping, showing or doing dressage. For each one of them it's a huge personal triumph, and they are rightly proud of what they and their horses have achieved, sometimes with the support of their vets and farriers, and sometimes despite all opposition.

For horses like these, which have been given no realistic chance of long-term improvement with conventional treatments, barefoot is a great choice. Even if there is only a limited evidence base for barefoot as a therapy, and even if it does not improve every horse, the facts are that it is a non-invasive option, and a natural state that horses are born to.

There is no doubt that the more invasive and aggressive an intervention is, the more evidence should be required in its support – but taking off a horse's shoes is neither invasive nor aggressive. If, on the other hand, you are considering operating on a horse, or nailing on corrective shoes, then in my opinion you should produce some fairly compelling evidence that the potential benefits are likely to outweigh the potential harm (not to mention expense) before you decide to do so.

Although taking a horse barefoot should be a relatively easy decision, especially when it follows a lameness diagnosis, I do feel that some vets and owners cannot resist needlessly complicating matters. With today's proliferation of insurance-driven veterinary treatment, it's almost as if a therapy is not worth trying if it is simple, cost effective, and readily comprehensible to the owner.

In the position we are in currently, when so many therapies are routinely used in horses even when clinical evidence is, at best, patchy (including many of the therapies routinely used to help lameness), and when other treatments have been used for years with no evidence beyond the anecdotal (much remedial farriery, for example), it is surely time to be level-headed and acknowledge that – although we need more research because our understanding of healthy hoof function and how to restore it is so limited – barefoot can offer long-term, low-risk, sustainable benefits to the knowledgeable and committed owner, which we are only beginning to fully appreciate.

The horse whose feet were shown during rehab in the previous pair of images. He now completes in affiliated dressage and eventing barefoot.

I have been trying to facilitate research into the hoof for a long time, and for the last eight years have been actively gathering data on the horses that have come through Rockley in the hopes of encouraging the veterinary institutions to look at this and compare the results with their conventional treatments. So far there has been a lot of interest from owners, quite a bit from vets who have sent horses here, but none from the veterinary institutions, even though I have regularly submitted data to them.

In fact, owners of former rehab horses would be only too happy for their horses to be reassessed by the same vets who originally diagnosed them – they are even keen for their horses to have follow-up MRI if necessary – but although I have discussed this idea with a number of academics and vets, so far there has been no interest in taking this type of study forwards, even though it would be far more cost-effective than the initial MRIs. We shall see what the next few years hold.

One of the helpful aspects of the data we have on horses that have undergone rehabilitation at Rockley is that many of them came to us after conventional therapies had been tried and had failed. There is a strong argument (which was made by a vet, not by me) for saying that once a horse has been diagnosed with (for example) a deep digital flexor tendon injury, and has been treated unsuccessfully with remedial farriery, medications and management changes such as box rest, then he acts as his own control for these therapies against a subsequent barefoot rehabilitation.

This would be one way of contrasting the success of barefoot rehabilitation with conventional therapies (research comparing the success of different treatments is also thin on the ground), but there is another factor that we need to bring into the equation: barefoot rehabilitation is also often tried when all other options have been tried but have failed. An eminent consultant surgeon and medical research specialist made a good point to me a few years ago, when I was bemoaning the lack of interest in carrying out research comparing barefoot with conventional therapies for horses with palmar hoof pain: he said, 'You don't run a double blind, randomized controlled trial for parachutes.'

Of course when a horse has been diagnosed as lame, owners and vets should look carefully at all the evidence before trying barefoot as a treatment option, and should weigh up potential benefits and harms – but they should do this for any other therapy or treatment option which is being evaluated as well. Both owners and vets also need to bear in mind how limited the evidence is for so many (much more aggressive) conventional veterinary therapies.

The records we have kept of the rehab horses that have come to Rockley, plus follow-up discussions with owners, covers a reasonably large number of horses (over ninety, with responses from owners on seventy-seven when we called them for the 2015 update). It showed that just under 80 per cent had returned to the same level of work or higher following rehab. These records do not include a control group, although we were told at one time that we would be able to use comparative data from a well-known veterinary school showing horses with the same diagnoses who had undergone conventional treatment; sadly this has not been forthcoming. However, many of the horses could 'act as their own controls' for the other treatments they have undergone.

The latest data we submitted to BEVA in 2016 focused solely on horses diagnosed with DDFT, impar ligament and navicular bone damage on MRI. Of these horses, 77.5 per cent were back in full work, and had been for at least a year, with the oldest still in work eight years after rehabilitation.

HORSES, SHOES AND RESEARCH

As an absolute minimum I think the most urgent need is for a deeper understanding of what a truly healthy hoof looks like, and how it functions. This is something that would be equally valuable for equine professionals – including vets and farriers – and for owners. We also need a thorough appreciation of how shoeing affects the strength and development of the palmar hoof, and whether it has a detrimental effect on the circulatory and vascular systems within the hoof capsule.

It will come as no surprise that I think shoes often do long-term damage to hooves. I've seen with the horses that come here for rehabilitation that the ones who have been out of shoes for a long time, or even better who have never been shod, recover at a faster rate and are easier to manage during rehabilitation (in other words are capable of harder work more quickly) than the horses that come in shoes, or that are recently out of shoes.

The practical problem is that it is likely to prove difficult to conduct this sort of research. Why? Finding healthy hooves isn't too difficult as there are increasing numbers of hardworking barefoot horses out there, and owners are more than willing to assist in this sort of research by making their own horses available and providing data and veterinary records; I know because so many of them have told me so.

So research into the function of hardworking bare hooves is a possibility. The more problematic research would be assessing how a shoe impacts on the health of a foot. The challenge arises because although plenty of studies have been done on shod versus unshod horses,

A foot on the same horse, on the left in shoes before rehabilitation; below, sound and after working barefoot for many months. The contrast in hairline shows the change in the digital cushion.

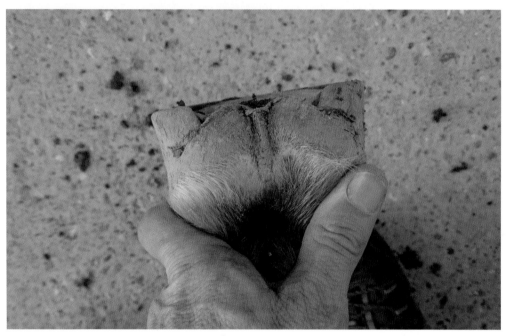

these almost always involve horses being assessed in shoes and then reassessed out of shoes. Sometimes it is two different groups, in other studies it's the same horses in and out of shoes, but the 'unshod' group rarely comprises horses with truly healthy bare hooves.

Although these studies give you an idea of how a shoe affects a weak foot, it does not give you any idea of how differently a healthy, hardworking bare foot functions compared to a shod foot. Nor does it give you any information (other than in purely mechanical terms) of the effect a shoe has on a healthy hoof over the longer term – or specifically what internal structures are compromised by the shoe.

As those of us who have rehabilitated horses know all too well, a shod horse will generally have a weak hoof compared to a hardworking barefoot horse, even when both horses have been on an optimal diet and in consistent work.

The shod foot will be used to loading peripherally, and will often also have a thinner sole (presumably due either to lack of stimulus or the method of trimming) than a barefoot horse. Shoes also generally seem to lead to horses having a weaker digital cushion, frog and heels than a barefoot horse (contrast the previous photos), and consequently these are less able to be effective shock absorbers than a barefoot horse that has a robust palmar hoof. Overall, a horse straight out of shoes is almost never going to have an optimally healthy hoof.

Combine these factors with the reality that most horses used in research programmes are not in work, and you can see that even the studies comparing unshod and shod hooves that do exist will not have been carried out with the benefit of truly healthy hooves, either as a comparison or a control, or as a benchmark from which to measure changes.

A further problem is that when you look at the small print of many studies there is little detail on the starting soundness (or otherwise) of the horses involved. For example, a recent piece of research footage produced by a farrier measured landing changes in shod and unshod horses 'under laboratory conditions' – but there were only two horses involved, neither was in work, and there was no information as to the horses' soundness either before, during, or after the various experiments – which for me made the video useless for all practical purposes.

To date there are no studies, as far as I am aware, that take a healthy, high-performing bare hoof and measure how it lands and loads, nor studies that measure the changes in function in such a foot once it is shod and over several cycles of shoeing. This is the research we need, but I cannot see any owners, no matter how supportive of research, allowing their healthy, high-performing barefoot horses to be shod over the medium to long term.

The closest alternative, as I mentioned earlier, might be to take two groups of genetically similar young horses – thoroughbreds would be the obvious choice – and shoe one group as normal (at under two years of age in the case of horses bred to race on the flat), while maintaining the other group barefoot under optimal conditions, and compare their hoof structure and function at intervals.

WHAT DO SHOES REALLY DO?

Recently I read a well-meaning comment by an equine professional. She is a long-time horse owner, and has experienced for herself how well horses can work without shoes, but her comment was that although she kept her own horses without shoes, she 'didn't recommend barefoot because there was so much to learn before you make the leap'.

I know exactly what she means and I sympathize, because if horses with weak feet, and which are on a poor diet, have their shoes taken off with no care or preparation, they will very often be sore – so taking shoes off a horse should not be recommended lightly. However, if you give these same horses an optimal diet for six to eight weeks and then assess their hoof health and biomechanics properly, they will more likely than not come straight out of shoes and carry on without any hesitation at all.

Here is the paradox. Those of us who keep our horses barefoot are often cautious about encouraging other owners to take their horses out of shoes, because although it can be both beneficial and rewarding, we are aware of the level of responsibility it puts on to the owner. We are also only too aware that taking the shoes off is just the tip of the iceberg, particularly if your horse has weak feet.

However, no one warns owners about the dangers of shoeing, although frankly the longer you have barefoot horses the more bizarre shoeing seems – did I really not think twice about asking my (lovely!) farrier to routinely bang six or eight nails into my horse's feet every five weeks? This is even though there are almost certainly more horses lamed by being shod than ever there are by going barefoot – not to mention the long-term deterioration that we see routinely in horses that have been shod year in, year out. If I were playing devil's advocate I would say that the barefoot fraternity are being more honest about the pros and cons than the shoeing fraternity – but perhaps the latter simply aren't aware of the problems.

There is no doubt that unquestioning tradition is a huge factor in why horses are shod. 'Confirmation bias' is a term used in cognitive science to describe what happens when people actively seek out evidence that supports what they are practising, and ignore evidence that would undermine it – does this sound at all familiar? Confirmation bias isn't confined to the shod horse fraternity: you can find examples of it among barefoot horse owners as well, but at least most of the latter have already had to question and change their past practices, and tend to (or should) start with a more open mind.

THE SCIENCE OF SHOES

There are, of course, a few published research studies available that investigate shoes and their effects. These are not randomized trials, but tend to be small studies that have been performed on relatively low numbers of horses (often fewer than thirty, and frequently with a sample group in single figures); furthermore these often measure just one particular variable, such as the effect of a bar shoe or wedge, and normally without a control group. There are even fewer studies into the effects of shoes as a treatment, or that compare shoeing to other treatments.

An article published in 2007 (Ehud Eliashar BSc, DVM, Dipl. ECVS, MRCVS at equipodiatry. com) summarizes a significant amount of research on the effect of shoes. He notes that 'relatively little research has been carried out into the fundamental aspects of shoeing, resulting in a lack of basic scientific knowledge.' A serious drawback that he highlights is that studies have typically

> … been performed using sound horses … Thus, while the information obtained from such studies is interesting, its direct clinical relevance is speculative, and the strength of evidence is not as strong as is desirable. There is a significant deficit in veterinary knowledge regarding the effects of shoeing and farriery techniques on clinically affected lame horses.

However, there are a few truths about shoes that can be stated with certainty. First, shoes increase concussion (see ref.: 'The effect of shoeing on kinetics and kinematics during the stance phase', Roeperstorff et al EVJ 1999 Jul (30) 279–85). It is self-evident that metal is more concussive than the unshod hoof capsule, but as well as the effect of metal transmitting concussion directly to, and into, the hoof capsule, there is in my view an equally important secondary effect from shoes. This is because in a long-term shod hoof the digital cushion and frog are generally less robust than in a long-term bare hoof. These structures play an important role in absorbing shock as the foot lands, and their function can clearly be seen if you watch a healthy barefoot horse walking away from you on a hard surface.

The best way to assess this for yourself is by feel: a healthy digital cushion is dense and bouncy and will completely fill the space at the back of the hoof which lies above the hairline and the frog and between the lateral cartilages of the hoof. If you feel the same area in a horse that has been long-term shod, the lateral cartilages will often be quite pronounced and there will be little material in the gap between them.

A shoe also increases load directly onto the areas of the hoof to which it is nailed or glued. Ironically both farriers and vets frequently say that they use shoes to provide 'support' for the horse. That sounds laudable, but the reality is that it's a mathematical impossibility (using the equation that pressure equals force divided by area) for any normal shoe to provide more support for the foot than a bare hoof. On soft ground the shoe may load a surface area only slightly smaller than a bare hoof, but as soon as the horse is on hard ground the loading area will be no more than the surface area of the shoe, a considerably smaller loading area than the heels, frog, sole and hoof wall which would be loaded in the same foot unshod.

Why? Because (as can be seen in the photos below), in the vast majority of shod horses, the hooves will load almost entirely round the hoof wall on hard ground with the frog and sole coming into play only on softer surfaces. Although some farriers aim for the frog to have contact with the ground even in a shoe, the amount of weight the frog takes is very limited by comparison with a bare foot – something which is easy to spot when you compare the prints of bare and shod hooves on hard surfaces, as we did on the snowy road in the photo.

Occasionally farriers will try to increase the load-bearing area of the shoe with extensions or edges, usually to provide 'support' to a weak area of the foot – often the palmar hoof. Some farriers even give this as a reason why they prefer shoes over barefoot. But the horse, when barefoot, already has this fantastic support called 'the ground', which extends for miles in every direction – in front, behind and all around – so how is extending the branch of a shoe going to provide more support to the hoof? It will certainly have a lever effect on break-over, and possibly on landing, but is that really going to be beneficial for a compromised hoof?

A shoe tends to result in the weight of the horse being taken on the periphery of the foot, as we can also see in these photos. This peripheral loading has a number of self-evident effects, including reducing stimulus to the sole and hoof wall, and making it much more difficult for the horse to maintain ideal foot balance through the whole shoeing cycle – but it also puts enormous stress on the laminae that bind the hoof wall to the internal hoof capsule. The more that weight is loaded on to the hoof wall and the less on to frog, sole and heels, the greater

The stark contrast in loading between barefoot and shod feet.

this stress becomes, to the point where in severe cases it is even possible for mechanical laminitis to occur.

In humans, shoes diminish proprioception (defined as the ability to sense where one's body is and how it is moving without the need for visual feedback), and there is no reason to suppose this is any different for horses – in fact as horseshoes are generally fixed on to the hoof the whole time, it would be logical for the effect to be, if anything, more severe than in a human foot, though there is (again) no research to prove this at the moment.

Shoes increase the risk of injury – to the horse itself, to other horses it may kick or knock intentionally or unintentionally, and of course to the humans who are around the horse. Any horse can strike into itself or tread on your foot, but if the horse is barefoot neither of you is likely to come to much harm by comparison with the same injury from a shod foot – and I am speaking from experience of both shod and bare hooves.

There is one final thing that shoes do very effectively: they allow a weak foot to perform instantly, as if it were much healthier and much stronger. On a truly healthy foot they won't improve performance, but as we all know, there are a lot of horses out there with poor feet. As I've said already, this effect of shoes is in my opinion the number one reason for the continuing popularity of shoes, and is absolutely the reason that shod horses outnumber barefoot horses in competitive disciplines, where time and rapid results are, frequently, money.

So if shoes can provide a quick fix for weak hooves, how do they do this? It is actually not exactly clear. Some farriers believe it's because the shoe restricts expansion and contraction in the hoof; this is one plausible explanation, as a weak foot with a poorly connected hoof capsule may well experience discomfort as it impacts on harder surfaces. Another possibility is that the shoe reduces circulation sufficiently that the horse does not sense the discomfort of a hard surface; this might explain why shod horses often show quite severe bruising in their feet without correspondingly severe lameness. A third factor may be that the shoe physically holds the hoof clear of the ground to a small degree, reducing the pressure of uneven ground on the frog and sole; this might explain why horses whose frogs and soles have been aggressively trimmed before shoeing are nevertheless able to walk away sound when shod, when without a shoe they would undoubtedly be sore.

As with barefoot, we simply don't have the categorical answers because the research doesn't really exist. The lack of data about the effects of shoes can definitely be a source of frustration, particularly to those of us whose experience leads us to believe that shoes are far from benign. However, this lack of data is equally a source of frustration to farriers and vets. Farrier David Gill prefaces his book (*Farriery: The Whole Horse Concept*) by saying:

> … *for the last two thousand years or so farriers … have been applying shoes to hooves … How deeply disappointing it is, then, that this collective build-up of experiences and knowledge has continually suffered from a lack of communication and a strong reluctance to share.*

Recently a new shoe was discussed by a group of farriers online. It was being used by a remedial farrier who is an advocate of research-led training, and its application was being taught to his students. There were a number of claims being made about the shoe – particularly that it reduced strain on laminae and collateral ligaments and so reduced lameness. There was also a claim that the shoe had 'been shown – scientifically – to increase the efficiency of motion to the hoof's gait'.

The problem was that the farrier concerned had not identified either what movement was causing the lameness, or what the 'increased efficiency' was, and whether this would correlate with a reduction of strain to the injured tissue. To make matters worse, while a farrier was

A bare hoof has a fantastic ability to absorb concussion, perfect for jumping.

claiming that the shoe reduced lamellar load (allowed the hoof to load more centrally), an engineer asserted that the design of the shoe made that impossible, and that the load would primarily be peripheral (taken by the hoof wall); furthermore the shoe itself had not been tested, so who do you believe?

The farrier concluded by admitting simply that – as with most remedial shoes – 'these shoes will work on some [horses] and make others more unsound'. Although there were references to 'science', and although he had the laudable objective of making the horse comfortable, there was no attempt, once the shoes were on, to analyse how they affected the loading or landing of the horse's feet, and no assessment of whether they would help or harm the horse in the medium or long term.

I am sure this farrier was acting with the best of intentions and trying to do his utmost for the horses in his care, but the discussion – while not an exhaustive exposition of the shoes – highlighted one of the biggest problems with shoeing: that the effects of a shoe on gait and biomechanics are not consistent from horse to horse, and are often poorly understood even by the very professionals who are using and fitting them.

This is a problem which is also found with trimming, of course. I am sure we can all give examples of trimmers, as well as farriers, who have left horses less sound, just as there are others who do an excellent job. It is critical, with both trimming and shoeing, to have a thorough understanding of what movement is healthy and beneficial, and what is not, well before you make any attempt to change it. This is even more important, if that's possible, when you are trying to help a horse recover from injury. Without being aware of, and isolating, the movement that is causing injury, it is fairly difficult to do anything to improve it, other than on a random basis.

It's not part of my brief to criticize farriers or trimmers, and I am certain that many of them are as frustrated as I am by the lack of research that is available. For research to be of practical use, however, we need a clear understanding of what constitutes a healthy hoof, the biomechanics of injury, and which movements (such as toe-first landings) contribute to ongoing strain. Following that, we need to ensure that farriers, vets and trimmers are much more systematic in the way they evaluate the movement of the horses in their care, and the effect that their trimming and shoeing has on that movement.

BAREFOOT AND THE VETERINARY PROFESSION

The feedback I receive consistently from vets who have direct, hands-on experience of hardworking barefoot horses is that these hooves come as a revelation to them. It's only after seeing healthy, rock-crunching hooves that they realize what a vast number of unhealthy hooves they have seen previously. In fact some admit they had never previously encountered a fully healthy hoof.

Talking to veterinary students it's clear that what they are being taught even today focuses almost entirely on a shod hoof, and there is an overwhelming expectation that horses will be routinely shod. However, I know that an increasing number of students find this frustrating. Some have become interested following their own experiences of taking horses barefoot, while others make it a topic for their own research projects, which is encouraging even though they are in the minority.

I am not really sure why there is so little veterinary teaching about barefoot, even though, among horses and owners, it is becoming steadily more popular and more common and is something owners want to discuss and understand. You might argue that it's because there is little research about barefoot, but that wouldn't explain why there is such a heavy emphasis on shoes as there is little research on shoes, either, certainly not enough to justify shoeing as the norm – particularly when, as we have seen, there is no research contrasting hardworking shod and barefoot horses to establish how hoof function is affected by shoes.

My suspicion is that the present-day reliance on shoes is largely the result of nothing more scientific than tradition. Whatever the reason, it will take a lot to change the status quo, not least because the present generation of veterinary students will finish their courses with no experience of barefoot or really healthy hooves during their training, unless they are fortunate enough to spend time in one of the rare practices that has hardworking barefoot horses on the books. Ironically my experience is that these sorts of horses rarely need to see a vet – and even more rarely for lameness – thus reducing students' experience even more.

Of course, one result of the traditional dependence on shoes – and the expectation that working horses used to 'need' shoes – is that those of us who have hardworking barefoot horses are almost without exception owners who previously had experience of shod horses. In fact, as I said at the beginning, a huge number of horses are taken barefoot simply because shoes have failed to keep them sound. By contrast, there are far fewer advocates of shoes who have experience of hardworking barefoot horses. When it comes to barefoot, the traffic is mostly one way – plenty of owners go from shoes to barefoot, but I know of relatively few who go from barefoot to shoes.

There is no doubt that the increasing interest in barefoot is at the moment led by owners, not vets. Nevertheless, although the veterinary profession as an institution has shown little interest, it is encouraging that individual vets who have hands-on experience of healthy hooves and their impressive ability to perform usually become enthusiastic supporters.

Hardworking barefoot horses on a Sunday morning.

CHAPTER 10

Rehabilitation of the Whole Horse

It's the job of the hoofcare professionals to thoroughly understand the movement we are aiming to facilitate in the horse, and equally, the movement we are trying to help the horse avoid. There may be a number of ways to achieve this, but the important thing is to monitor the horse before and after any intervention, and honestly record what effect we are having on him, not just on the first day but over the succeeding weeks and months. It's just not enough nowadays simply to trot a horse up and have a look at it – not least because it's both easy and almost instant nowadays to do a more thorough analysis. We should make full use of the technology available to us, and this particularly applies to anyone who is trying an experimental technique, such as the new shoe that was discussed in the previous chapter.

Common areas of secondary pain in a lame horse.

The golden rule, in my opinion, should be that if something is not working for the h.
– in other words, if his movement and soundness are not improving – or, heaven forbid,
getting worse – over, say, a four-week period, then something has to change.

Although very often analysis of movement and soundness will start at the feet, I think it is
essential that we also look at the whole horse. Vets, physiotherapists and other body work-
ers are only too aware that an issue such as lameness will also have knock-on effects on the
shoulders, back and neck of the horse, resulting in muscle soreness initially; if the restriction
goes on for long enough then you may even see related muscle wastage and asymmetry.

Over time if the lameness continues then the horse will compensate to accommodate the
restriction the lameness brings – for instance, he may have to shorten his hind-limb stride if
he can no longer fully extend his front legs. The areas highlighted in the previous photo are
common areas of secondary pain and injury in horses with front limb lameness.

So along with an understanding of limb and foot biomechanics we need an understanding of how the rest of the body is affected. Very often, once the original lameness is resolved
the horse will default back into better patterns of movement simply because these are more
comfortable and efficient; however, this isn't always the case, and if the movement does not
improve despite the original problem no longer being the cause (and it's always sensible
to double check that this has in fact happened, and that there is no underlying niggle still
remaining), then that is when additional help will be required.

Establishing balance and flexibility helps to reduce the risk of injury.

˙ talk about the importance of straightness in horses, and straightness has
of a mantra amongst riders and owners. 'Straightness training' is a new
.ically classical, correct training, but 'classical' is a word misused almost as
.atural' so, as with anything, it's important to know exactly what we are aiming

.ect training can certainly help the horse, but when dealing with a horse coming back
.om injury we need to be particularly mindful of what we are asking of him. We need to know, specifically, why movements need to change, and which old patterns of movement have been causing harm.

Most horses, like most people, have a natural asymmetry, and the aim of straightness training is to develop and balance the horse, enabling greater strength on the weaker side and greater flexibility on the stiffer side so that the horse is more symmetrical and can work more evenly on both reins. That's a laudable aim and can have very positive results, but in my experience it doesn't work in isolation; as you might expect, the best results are achieved when you start from the ground up.

In the case of a lame horse you need to establish a basic level of soundness – in other words, to establish that a recent injury has healed – before trying to correct an asymmetry, since asking a horse to increase the load on a lame leg would be counter-productive. This doesn't mean that you need perfect movement – the aim of training, after all, is to improve movement – but you need to be happy that the corrective training you are asking from the horse is enhancing rather than hindering the healing process. If diagnostic tools such as ultrasound are available then they can be very useful, but often introducing gentle, easy work and monitoring the horse's movement is the most practical way to assess this.

In my experience, even when horses are bilaterally lame, one leg is almost always worse than the other. It is commonly the left front leg – this is the case with most, though certainly not all, horses. By an interesting coincidence (or is it?) most (but not all) horses also find it easier to bend to the left than the right. Because the horse's head and neck are a significant part of the weight on the front legs, effectively this means that they will more readily put extra weight on the left leg than the right leg. So the question is: are these horses lamer on the left leg because it is carrying more weight, or because the injury is worse on the left? And if the injury is worse on the left, is this because that leg is carrying more weight?

For all practical purposes it doesn't really matter. The solution is the same – to encourage better movement and better balance to allow the injury to heal, and to establish good patterns of movement to ensure that it has less chance of re-injury.

Mismatched hooves (high heel/low heel) often cause concern and are a focus of corrective training. However, these hooves are usually a symptom, not a cause, of unbalanced movement. The low hoof will tend to be the side the horse is overloading, while the high hoof will be the weaker side. Straightness training works on rebalancing the horse, but you also need to be improving the horse's dynamic hoof balance so that he is more comfortable and competent to load both hooves evenly.

What you can't do is concentrate on only one problem and ignore the other. You can't establish real soundness simply and only by enabling the horse to be straighter, more symmetrical and less one-sided. After all, looking at the horse that bends more easily left, if you enable him to bend right as easily as left, then the chances are that he will be weighting his front legs more evenly. This may improve the lameness on the left leg, but a bilaterally lame horse is still lame, even if it is harder to spot.

Equally, if you focus on the feet and enable the horse to grow stronger, healthier hooves and to stop landing toe first, he will certainly become sounder and his lameness may go completely

– but he will still be more flexible on one side than the other (which may or may not matter, depending on what work he is being asked to do), and therefore predisposed to re-injury.

It's always tempting to focus only on what you are most familiar with (in my case hooves; in the case of some others, straightness), but that won't help the whole horse. The best option – certainly for a ridden horse – is to aim for both: strong, healthy hooves as the precursor to allowing the horse to become more flexible and balanced through his body.

However, I have repeatedly seen with feet that, while symmetry is desirable in a perfect world, apparent asymmetry is often the horse's response to injury, and it is sometimes an essential compensation that is required for good balance and proper function. It is therefore very important to distinguish between the times when we should aim for symmetry, and the times when asymmetry should be respected and allowed to stand. Generally, the final arbiter is how the horse is moving – this is, after all, what he has evolved to do. A horse that is moving better with an apparent asymmetry than he is without should be allowed, in my view, to have the last word, since there is likely to be a very good biomechanical reason (which may not be apparent to us) for the asymmetry.

INITIAL REHABILITATIVE WORK

My own experience with rehab horses here is that once a correct landing is in place, in-hand work can be very beneficial. It can encourage horses to move more evenly, and to begin, for instance, to get out of a restricted, habitual way of moving which they have had to adopt while injured. In-hand work can encourage them to explore more balanced ways of moving – for example, beginning to put more load on a healed but weaker limb, which they may have been guarding for months during injury.

Similarly, with horses that have had a long-term front-limb lameness, and which have developed a hollow, tense way of going as a way of taking weight off their front legs, in-hand work is a great way of allowing them to develop freer movement, stretching down and lifting their backs. This usually happens quite naturally once they are more comfortable in front, if they are worked gently and allowed to experiment. Initially a horse may show only a few strides of better movement, but in the next session there should be more.

The secret is to allow and encourage rather than force, since using force usually just sets up resistance and often perpetuates the bad movement we are trying to get rid of. For this reason I work horses using only a cavesson and lunge line. I don't use any gadgets or side-reins as I need the horse to be completely free to experiment, and to have nothing against which he can brace.

Horses, like us, are normally only too willing to adopt a more comfortable, more efficient and easier way of going if they are given half a chance, so if you have a horse that is resolutely stuck in a bad pattern of movement it may well be because you haven't yet found the root of the problem.

Since straight lines are easier for limbs than circles, another good form of early work is leading the horse out from another horse, or long-reining him. I like to start this way, rather than under saddle, as it allows the horse to build muscle and fitness before dealing with the weight of a rider. Extra weight on the back can also be too much in the initial stages of rehabilitation, whereas the easy mileage you can do leading or long-reining is less challenging but great for feet. A horse that is coming back into work after injury will also be much calmer, and back in a routine, once he has had a few weeks of this sort of work, which can make your first ridden sessions less stressful.

Ride and lead is a good form of rehabilitative exercise.

With any rehabilitative work, whether in hand or under saddle, it's important to start with very short, easy sessions, and to give the horse a day off in between each session at the beginning. If you are on the right track the horse should show steady improvement over, say, a two-week period; if the horse is struggling, then stop, reduce the work level, make everything even easier, check that his landing is heading in the right direction, and then try again.

I am often asked for what a suitable work programme might be for a horse coming back from lameness, but the truth is that there is no one-size-fits all. It's for that reason that I don't include set routines in here – they may suit one horse, but be wrong for another. Rather than relying on a template, it's important to be guided by the horse himself. There are lots of ways to improve movement and soundness, but bear in mind that only good movement will build good movement.

For me, soundness in a horse is not absolute, but is conditional. For example, a horse may be sound in walk in a straight line, but lame in trot; a much more capable horse may be sound in walk and trot in a straight line, but show unlevelness on a tight circle. Generally, the tougher the surface, the sharper the turn and the higher the speed, the more strain it puts on the horse's limbs and feet, and the sounder he must be to be perfectly balanced and level.

When I am working a horse I will only work him within the zone where he can work soundly. If this means he can only work in walk, on a soft surface, then so be it. However, after a period of correct rehabilitation and time working within this zone you should find that the zone has expanded slightly – perhaps he can work for longer, or can now offer a few sound steps of trot, or can cope with a harder surface, even for a short time. The great benefit of working this way is that the horse usually enjoys his work, as you aren't asking him for something painful or impossible.

Straightness and classical training is probably best taught in person, but there are resources online. One good website is http://www.ttttrust.com, where you can find information about clinics and trainers; you can also find some online advice at Marijke de Jong's website, where there are plenty of useful resources and tips.

CHARTING PROGRESS

When you (or your vet or body worker) are assessing your horse for progress (or otherwise) the best option is to use video footage. Whereas this would once have been quite an undertaking, it's very easy nowadays as so many of us can take good quality footage with our phones. It's important to make improvements as measurable as possible, so try to film in the same place and from the same angle. You can then compare like with like, and assess movement and soundness over the weeks and months, rather than day by day, which helps to give a better perspective.

Frequently rehabilitation has its ups and downs – it's rarely a smooth, linear upward curve, and it can sometimes feel like two steps forwards, one step back. The best way to assess progress (or lack of it) is to keep detailed notes and to use this and your film footage so that you and your team (vet, body worker and any hoofcare professional) can decide whether you are on the right track.

If your horse is not improving, then of course it's back to the drawing board. It's often helpful to go through your notes and check whether anything has changed, as almost all problems have a cause, if only we can spot it; identifying the trigger is sometimes the hardest part. You can check the chapters later on in this book for common foot issues and how to solve them.

Most owners don't need reminding, but it's always worth remembering that horses can only show us how they are feeling through their behaviour, so if that is changing then it's always for a reason. This cuts both ways – a horse that is uncharacteristically 'nappy', 'naughty' or 'sharp' is most often (in my experience) a horse in discomfort; equally a horse that is becoming more relaxed, less reactive and more confident is probably becoming sounder and stronger.

HELPFUL ADVICE? ASSESSING YOUR 'EXPERT'

This is probably the place to add a few words about the well intentioned advice and wisdom always on offer (sometimes at a high price) from the myriad experts who abound in the equestrian world. Over the years I've met a lot of experts: there are good ones, bad ones, brilliant ones, mediocre ones, safe ones, scary ones. The one thing they have in common is that they will all offer you advice, and plenty of it. Speaking as someone who has been bamboozled on a few occasions, enlightened on many, and who has ignored at least as much advice as I have acted on, it can be very hard to pick out the worthwhile advice from the stuff that is best consigned to oblivion.

After a lot of trial and error, there are four tests that I always go back to, and which I think are worth bearing in mind as a way of judging the value of an expert's contribution.

Firstly, do they really have the expertise I need? I have had countless people tell me that they want to take their horse barefoot, but that their farrier or vet has said it's impossible; however, I have never, ever heard that statement from someone whose vet or farrier was actually experienced in working horses barefoot. I have had many useful discussions with

Always see what is really there.

excellent farriers for whom I would have great respect if they were shoeing my horses. However, there was only one whom I would trust with a barefoot horse.

If you are looking for hoof advice, it pays to be selective. As my hoofcare colleague Steve Leigh says:

> *You wouldn't pick a driving instructor who often crashes, you wouldn't pick a shooting instructor who couldn't hit a clay, so apply the same principle. Do they have horses? Are they field ornaments, or do they work hard? Look at their other clients – you want someone who can help horses work consistently across all disciplines.*

My second tip is a great quote which Sir Terry Pratchett used to put into the mouths of a number of his most interesting Discworld characters: 'Always see what is really there.' At a time when there are so many experts out there vying for the attention of you, the consumer, and who are ready to dissemble with clever props or weasel words to make what they are doing seem kinder or better than it really is, it pays to look beyond the marketing and see the horse. What is *he* telling you? With the sound off and no salesman's patter to distract, what is really happening?

I am always suspicious of any trainer who depends on fancy dress (and that for me includes cowboy hats – it's fine to wear one in the US, but it's definitely fancy dress if you are in the UK) or slick marketing to distract from how the horse is responding. I was once at a clinic with a trainer like this and decided that since he was in fancy dress (ten gallon hat, toggle shirt and fringed chaps... in Devon), I would turn up in (arguably more appropriate) full hunting kit – blue coat, hunt buttons, stock, horse plaited up. He didn't see the funny side, though it cheered my horse up enormously. Needless to say he was not someone I revisited.

Similarly the power of having a microphone and an audience can make bullies out of a lot of instructors. I am invariably suspicious of anyone who doesn't allow questions or squashes an alternative point of view (because there always is one) without explanation. Knowledge is power, but intelligent, even passionate questions are something any worthwhile expert should have answers for, and not be intimidated by.

One unique facet of the equine industry is that it has a disproportionately large number of female consumers – there are many more women than men at grass roots level, and so unsurprisingly they are generally the target audience for equine professionals. Once you get to the level of the equine professionals themselves, things are apparently more 'equal' (meaning that there are lots of males at this level), and this in practice means that there are many occasions when male trainers, vets, hoofcare providers and so on have a mostly female audience.

Of course there are plenty of excellent male trainers, vets and hoofcare providers who don't let it make a bit of difference who the audience is – their egos don't depend on having an audience of ladies hanging on their every word, and they will be as helpful and as passionate, and have just as much integrity no matter who they are speaking to. There are sadly others who seem more interested in cultivating their status as a (male) guru with compliant (female) acolytes than in empowering their audience or helping them progress. So if your 'expert' – whether trainer, vet or hoofcare provider – hates questions or discussions, is happy to hear about your problems but is less willing to help you move on from them, and is more interested in getting you to sign up to their programme than becoming self-reliant, then it's worth finding an alternative. I am aware that it is theoretically possible for there to be female trainers, vets and hoofcare providers who fall into the 'guru' class, but I have yet to come across any.

The third tip is a phrase that has become a mantra for me: ultimately, that the horse is the true 'expert'. In practice this means that if what a human 'expert' is telling me doesn't match what the horse is telling me, then the 'expert' is wrong and the horse is right. This goes for saddle fit, training, hoofcare – you name it. I've had numerous encounters with equine experts over the years, and many of them have made incredibly valuable contributions to my own learning – but whenever I have over-ruled the horse in favour of the 'expert' it has gone horribly wrong: the horse is always right in the end. I don't mean by this that I allow horses to push me around or dictate to me, but if (for example) the saddler is telling me the fit is fine, but the horse is clearly uncomfortable, I will believe the horse every single time. Similarly I will take the horse's side rather than the hoofcare 'expert' who says that he needs a trim, which makes him less sound, or the trainer who says he needs a gadget when he is clearly shouting 'no'.

The fourth and last point I try always to remember is that good intentions are ubiquitous – the best experts have them, but so do the worst – so good intentions are never enough. I have a favourite quote from Anna Sewell's *Black Beauty*, when our hero is nearly killed by a young groom, which speaks for itself:

'I know he meant no harm, I never said he did; I know he is not a bad boy …'

'Thank you John, I know you did not wish to be too hard, and I am glad you see it was only ignorance.'

John's voice almost startled me as he answered: 'Only ignorance! Only ignorance! How can you talk about only ignorance? Don't you know that it is the worst thing in the world, next to wickedness, and which does the most mischief, heaven only knows. If people can say "Oh! I did not know, I did not mean any harm," they think it is all right!'

To do the best for our horses and ourselves we need to be constantly questioning, constantly learning, and constantly trying to improve.

If horse and 'expert' disagree, trust the horse.

TWO HEADS ARE BETTER THAN ONE

I know that I am not the only person who has been saved by my horse from the consequences of my own folly. I will never forget riding my best hunter, Felix, home across Exmoor one day and deciding to go the most direct route as the weather was closing in. Crossing a piece of moorland and dropping down a valley, I knew we only needed to get to the other side and it would be a quick hack back to the road. Felix, totally uncharacteristically, stopped and refused to cross. I was a bit surprised but stupidly gave him a nudge and told him to get on with it. He still refused. I repeated my aid with a bit more exasperation, at which point he very deliberately picked up one front foot, inserted it up to the knee in the bog in front of us and turned his head, giving me a look whose meaning was transparently clear. Sufficiently prompted at last, I agreed to retrace our steps and find a different way across.

Years ago I remember being told by Lucinda Green in a cross-country clinic that jumping cross-country was a dual responsibility – the rider was in charge of the line and the speed, but the horse was in charge of the actual jumping. Eventer and coach Kim Walnes put it nicely in her online blog *The Way of the Horse* when she says:

> You want to be on a horse who is alive in the moment and thinking towards the same goal you have … I can't tell you the number of times I have been saved by my horse making independent split second decisions.

Having this sort of partnership with your horse is what I want and work towards. I don't want a horse who is merely an obedient automaton; instead I want a partnership where the communication goes both ways and where there is mutual respect and shared decision-making. Even just riding out, your horse needs to trust you and you need to trust your horse – it cuts both ways.

Sometimes I will insist that Charlie steadies up because I know there is bad ground ahead (I am usually right); sometimes he will insist that if we are to find the huntsman and hounds we need to go this way (he is usually right). I will listen to him, he will listen to me (most of the time) and we have a level of trust and communication which we have developed over the years. Charlie has hunted for eleven seasons; he has taken countless riders across Exmoor and is superbly good at his job, so there are lots of occasions when he gets to call the shots. However, he doesn't like really gale force winds and on these occasions needs his rider to remind him that he is as brave as a lion, has faced a lot worse and that we will be safe despite the weather.

If he comes out of the lorry and there are no hounds in evidence he needs to trust that we are, in fact, hacking to the meet and not just out exercising (after forty-five minutes you can feel his trust starting to become a little shaky, but he will persist; his relief when he finally sees or hears hounds is palpable). On these occasions, he trusts me and does as I ask despite his concerns; in return I respect the fact that nowadays he finds hacking out a bore (he simply stops and observes the scenery, ignoring any attempt to make him go forward), so if I need to take him exercising on a non-hunting day he is led from another horse, which he finds perfectly acceptable, trotting along at a great rate in a purposeful manner.

When Charlie stops out hacking, he isn't being naughty or spooky; he is merely bored. Forcing him to hack out won't make him any less bored and it is no fun for me either, so we don't do it. I wouldn't expect this to work for every horse and rider combination (I can think of a few horses I have known in the past where it would be disastrous), but it works for Charlie and me.

A partnership where communication goes both ways.

Riding should, to my mind, be about developing a good, solid partnership, whatever it is that you and your horse want to do, and being flexible enough not to have a one-size-fits-all approach. If dressage is your thing, there is little point in having a horse who finds working in an arena tedious. If you love hacking, you won't have much fun if your horse is an agoraphobic who is traumatized by the great outdoors (this may sound extreme but we have had both sorts of horses here for rehab – fortunately they and their owners had exactly the same likes and dislikes!).

Keeping horses is expensive and time-consuming and we do it (mostly) for fun so it is important to find something that you and your horse enjoy together. Of course, any partnership worth its salt will take time, training and patience to establish; but it should, on the whole, be a rewarding and enjoyable journey even if it has its ups and downs. If you can't honestly say that you and your horse are enjoying yourselves then in the interests of both of your sanity, as well as a happy partnership, it is probably time for one of you to do something else.

I think it is only with shared enjoyment that we can really develop a great partnership with our horses. My own experience has been that it is when you have a shared purpose that the best partnerships are forged, when you and your horse are working together on equal terms.

In contrast, I was at a clinic a couple of years ago where a well-known US horseman (another who was wearing a cowboy hat) made it clear in no uncertain terms that he prized obedience first and foremost. He told his audience that he did not permit his horses to become distracted or to distract him; if his horse noticed something outside the arena then the horse should be corrected. What he perceived as inattention from the horse should be neither acknowledged

You want your horse to be alive in the moment.

nor encouraged because the horse must concentrate wholly on what he, the rider, required. Interestingly, he made great play of the fact that his horses at home were 'working ranch horses', unlike the soft, 'pampered pets' that he found in the UK. I commented that over here we use tractors for farm work nowadays, having moved on from horsepower during the last hundred years, but he was sufficiently self-absorbed that this went straight over his head! It seemed sad to me that he ignored the feedback his horses were giving him. I was even more surprised because my limited understanding of Western riding was that (as in hunting and eventing) horses were taught to think for themselves, especially when working cows, so I would have expected independence to be encouraged in a good ranch horse. I later learned that the truth was that he had not had a ranch for a long time; his horses were turned away for many months of the year and spent most of the rest of their time ambling round arenas during his clinics. I am sure they were good, obedient horses in the arena but I am also sure that he would have struggled if he had attempted to take one of his so-called 'ranch' horses cross-country or over the sort of terrain we hunt on; I suspect they would not have been great at working cows either.

COMMUNICATION AND CONFIDENCE

It's lovely when owners have such a close relationship with the horse that communication between them is easy, even intuitive, but ironically this can sometimes be a double-edged sword. One of the features of rehab at Rockley is that the owner is not present on a day-to-day basis. This means that for a lot of the time it's just me and the horse and we simply get on and do whatever rehabilitation work he needs. Usually horses arrive with a fairly significant lameness and they have often been uncomfortable for a long time, but because I have seen so many horses in the same condition, the lameness in itself doesn't worry me. When the horse and I are working we try to ensure that it is within his comfort zone, and so over time the horses become pretty relaxed. Interestingly, when owners come down and visit, they very often remark that the horse is quieter than at home. I used to think this was all due to the remote location of the farm and the fact that our own horses are used to new arrivals and so rarely over-react but there may be another effect coming into play as well.

I have noticed since I first started taking horses' shoes off that the dynamic between me and the horse will often be different from the dynamic between the horse and his owner. It first became clear when I had a 'round' and was going out to see other people's horses on a regular basis. One of the first things I would do, especially with a horse and owner who were new to barefoot, was discuss with the owner how the horse had been getting on since my last visit and then we would walk and trot the horse up. We would often alternate who was leading the horse so that we both got the chance to see the horse moving and it was noticeable that the horses would often move better on tougher surfaces when I was leading them than when it was their owner on the end of the lead rope.

Over a few months of careful observation, I worked out what seemed to be happening. When I was leading the horse, I tended just to get on with it – I wasn't rough or abrupt, but I certainly had the mentality that we had a job to do and I was confident the horse could cope. You could paraphrase my intention as being 'Come along, off we go, best foot forward, no messing about'. The horses would usually respond the same way, stepping out purposefully and crossing even tough terrain without hesitation.

When I handed the lead rope to the owner and asked her to lead the horse over the same terrain, I very often saw a change come over both horse and owner. The owner was worried about over-facing the horse and the horse would only make tentative progress over the difficult surface. You could clearly read the owner's concerns in their body language; it was screaming to the horse 'This is going to hurt, I am afraid of asking you to move forward, I am unsure about what I am asking you to do.' Naturally the horse would become less sure of himself, he would tense up and his stride would shorten. Suddenly terrain that had been no problem a few moments ago was apparently causing the horse difficulty, although nothing in the surface or his hooves had changed at all.

Exactly the same thing can happen when owners come and visit their horse during rehabilitation. If the owner is worried, both she and the horse can almost 'freeze' once they are together again and the trepidation of the owner can have a direct and dramatic effect on

Close relationships between horse and rider are very powerful.

the horse's confidence. As they both become tense, this can also have an effect on how the horse is moving. Ironically, of course, the closer the relationship between horse and owner, the bigger this effect can be.

While having a good relationship with your horse and building his trust in you is essential, we need to be aware that our own emotions can directly affect our horses' behaviour. Anyone who has been around horses for any length of time will remember times when they were preoccupied or stressed or in a rush and their horse picked up on and reacted to that immediately. One of the horses I had many years ago felt so uncomfortable if I was in a bad mood that he would not let me near him in the field until I calmed myself down; the more I rushed and got annoyed with him being difficult to catch, the more distance he would put between us.

Conversely I am sure many of us can remember days when both horse and rider were able to feed off each others confidence, everything seemed to go right and we and our horses were perfectly in tune, performing better together than we ever imagined. When a horse has been lame or ill it's impossible not to worry about them, and the closer we are the more we will tend to worry. That's perfectly natural, but it's also important not to be swept away by those feelings and to allow them to cloud decision-making or to influence how we behave.

Our horses depend on us for so much that, I believe, they learn to read us extremely well. When a horse has been injured, we need to be aware of how our feeling and behaviour can affect them. It's not a case of trying to hide our feelings from them, but we need to stay positive and confident, for our own sakes as well as for theirs. We need to try to control our own levels of worry when we are around our horses, not only because worry is exhausting and very often useless for us, but also because if we do not act positively our horses can react to this and be adversely affected. I am not suggesting you pretend nothing is wrong or ignore the concerns and fears that you have; I know in many cases that just isn't possible.

However it is important to make clear decisions about the care of your horse and to stand by them with confidence and without apology once they are made. Do your research, be logical and careful and once you have made a decision, stick to it. If you choose to use remedial shoes for lameness, give them a fair chance. Be confident and give your horse and your farrier every support and every opportunity to improve. If you choose to take your horse barefoot, be equally confident, try your hardest, and let your horse benefit from your positive attitude. Of course if you are not sure what to do or have difficult choices to make it can be a tricky balancing act – you need to be persistent, but not blinkered; stalwart but not stubborn. If you aren't sure whether your first route is the right option to take, then do the best you can and be as honest, logical and transparent as you can be in your decision-making.

Generally with lameness you should be able to see improvements within at least four to six weeks if you are on the right track, so set a realistic timescale and be consistent. Make it clear that you are going to try plan A first and that if it's not successful you will stop that and opt for plan B instead; there is no harm in that and no-one expects you to be infallible.

CHAPTER 11

Troubleshooting: Real or Imaginary Troubles

There are many things that stop owners from taking or keeping horses barefoot, and many glitches they may encounter once they have a barefoot horse, but for me they fall into two categories. First there are the imaginary problems – problems that trouble the owner and may well be enough to make them stay with shoes or go back to shoeing their horse, but which don't in fact cause the horse any issues, whether lameness or otherwise. It can be as trivial as worrying what other people on the yard might think, fear that an instructor may not approve or may think the feet look odd, or even (I've really heard this!) that the owner misses the sound their horse's shoes make as they clip-clop down the road.

I call these 'imaginary' because I am looking at them from the horse's point of view. Of course the troubles are real for the owner, but it's equally only the owner who can solve them. If you are being badgered by people who are telling you your horse's feet should look differ-ent to how they do, but he is perfectly happy, then you need to decide whether to trust your horse, or the 'experts' – bearing in mind, of course, that although your horse may not have a degree, a website or professional experience, he does have fifty million years of hard-won evolutionary genius showing him how to grow a really, really efficient foot.

The second set of troubles are what I call the real problems – in other words, they are exter-nal factors that are having an effect on your horse's hooves and health. In many cases there are steps you can take to eradicate or at least improve the problem; occasionally the problem may be caused by external pressures or circumstances that are unavoidable. Is it something irrevocable, or is it capable of remedy? You are not going to be able to untangle which you are dealing with until you take a much closer look.

What I hope to do in this section is help you work out which problems you are faced with, and what you may be able to do about them.

HOOVES WEARING TOO SHORT

This is classically the sort of problem identified by people who are more used to looking at shod feet – very often farriers – and owners who are not used to the appearance of a hard-working bare foot.

For me, this falls into the category of an imaginary problem – a problem for the owner but not for the horse. Nevertheless it's often given as the reason for putting shoes on a horse that is coping perfectly well without them. The shoes are brought in as a 'preventative measure', and are thought to be essential in order to avoid the horse becoming sore.

Please don't misunderstand me. If the horse is really sore then of course it's not an

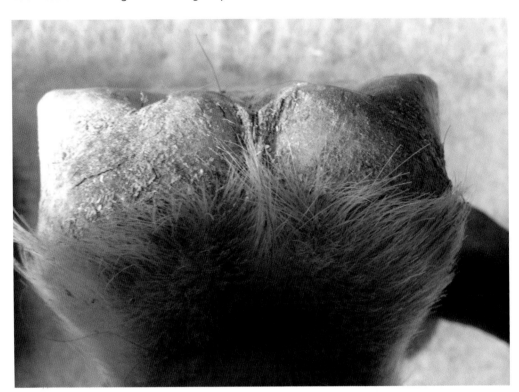

This hoof is not too short!

imaginary problem. But if you have a perfectly sound horse and you are worried that he may potentially become sore at some time in the future when his feet (which are fine for him now) might have worn down too much – that's definitely in your mind.

The fear of hooves being too short arises because we are all taught – farriers, vets and owners alike – that hooves wear at a set rate, and that every mile on the roads or on an abrasive surface such as sand wears them down. Thus we theorize that there is only a finite number of miles that hooves can take over a set period of time before they wear down to bloody stumps and the horse goes lame.

In reality the growth rate of hooves is incredibly adjustable and adaptable. Of course, if one were a totally callous and unfeeling rider it would be possible to take a horse straight out of shoes and cover so many miles over challenging terrain that the horse became sore. This almost never happens in the real world because most owners are aware of the feedback they receive from their horses, and are intelligent enough to realize that taking a horse out of shoes, initially, means a big change in how the feet function.

The truth of the matter is that most owners are so cautious when they first ride their horses barefoot that the greatest danger is not of them doing too many miles, but not enough. Over a period of weeks, usually, hooves adapt to a consistent workload, and normally the growth rate is more than adequate for the sort of mileage that most riders clock up.

With careful training and preparation of not just the hooves but the whole horse, endurance riders have successfully taken barefoot horses on single day rides of sixty kilometres in the UK, all with regular veterinary checks to confirm the horse's soundness.

Our own hunters will frequently have weeks when they cover fifty miles or more of varied terrain hunting, in addition to all their 'normal' mileage on our tracks, and their hoof growth rate has never failed to keep up with their mileage, allowing them to go week after week without their hooves ever becoming 'too short'.

There is no doubt, though, that if you are used to a shod hoof, then a bare hoof may look short. Essentially this is due to the different way the foot loads when it is shod: with a shoe the load is primarily taken on the hoof wall, which must be left long enough so that the shoe can be nailed on and avoid sole pressure.

With a bare hoof there is no need for this extra length of hoof wall, and in fact over-long hoof wall will quickly chip away once the horse is on anything other than the softest surface. Hooves 'chipping away' can also be a worry for those unused to a bare hoof; but again, this is rarely a problem for the horse, and so also falls into the category of 'imaginary' problems. The only time it would conceivably be a genuine problem is if you are wanting to put a shoe back on. We are back to whether you trust your horse to be the expert on his feet and soundness, or whether you are prepared to let someone else overrule him.

FOOTINESS AND ITS CAUSES

I am fairly confident that footiness is the single biggest problem that owners face when work-ing horses barefoot in the UK. It can be an issue equally for horses that have just come out of shoes, and for horses that have always been barefoot. It's a problem on livery yards and when horses are kept at home, and it's something that almost all of us will struggle with at one time or another. It's also probably the primary reason for owners who have tried barefoot to go back to shoes. I long ago lost count of the number of posts I have read on social media which began 'I took my horse's shoes off but he was sore so I had to go back to shoes...'.

I understand the frustration because I have been in exactly the same place, with a footy horse that seemed to be living proof that 'some horses just can't cope without shoes'.

Footiness is also something that many owners have to deal with when they take horses home from here. It can be a huge shock to an owner whose horse has come from Rockley, where the grass is safe and we also have grass-free turnout, seeing the effect on his soundness once he is turned out in the spring at his livery yard on fields of ryegrass. I imagine I am not the only one who refused to believe the problem was nutritional until I saw my footy horse miraculously rock-crunching once the diet was totally overhauled.

However, although diet is a big factor, it's not the only culprit. One of the difficulties with a footy horse is that there can be a lot of different contributory factors, and unravelling what is causing your problem can be a real headache, especially as some factors may not be under your control. However, you have to start somewhere, and I would always advise changing just one thing at a time so that you have the best possible chance of isolating the issues.

Nutrition

Nutrition is invariably where you should start if you have a footy horse. Nine times out of ten the problem will be either something the horse is eating, or something he needs that is not provided by his current diet.

Those of you who have never had a barefoot horse, and have, like me, blithely offered your shod horse conditioning cubes, barley rings and ad lib spring grass without realizing that this

Be careful of too much grass, especially in spring and summer.

was a factor in him being crippled on stony ground when he lost a shoe … well, suffice it to say that you, like me, will have a steep learning curve.

It's hard for any of us to believe until we have experienced it first hand, but hooves can be minutely affected by the horse's diet, and the commonest symptom of a nutritional glitch is footiness or sole sensitivity.

Forage

The number one culprit that will give many horses sole sensitivity is high sugar forage – most commonly horses having access to rich grass during peak growth periods. We often forget that horses evolved as a niche grazer, able to survive on high fibre, low calorie forage. Horses are able to thrive on land where cattle would starve, and yet we are surprised when modern pasture, seeded with a monoculture developed to be high in sugar and low in fibre, doesn't suit them. Horses also evolved to work hard for their food, and so it shouldn't come as a surprise that turnout in a field and a few hours work a week aren't nearly enough to burn off the high calorie forage we offer them.

The most dangerous times for grazing in the UK are traditionally the spring and summer, but grass can be equally risky during a warm autumn. Crucially, not all grazing will cause a problem, and not all horses will show the effects, so it's very much something to rule in or out on a case by case basis. It can be very individual – it is for our horses – so grazing whi< is safe for three of your horses may be too much for the fourth, who is, for whatever reason, more sensitive.

Often, grass is trickier to manage than other forage because sugar levels can fluctuate so dramatically depending on growing conditions. We are fortunate that our horses graze on old, safe pasture; only one is sensitive to our grass (and only if allowed prolonged, constant access) and none is sensitive to our haylage – but that isn't always the case.

Sugar levels fall rapidly once grass is cut, but hay can also be high in sugar, depending on when it is made and what grasses it is made from. If you are concerned, then soaking will reduce the sugar levels as well as being a sensible way to reduce the respiratory challenge of hay. Haylage is typically lower in sugar (and in any case shouldn't be soaked) but can also be risky if it's made from high sugar grass varieties; mixed-species meadow haylage is safer. Unfortunately the look and smell of forage can't tell you whether it's low in sugar, so it's only by trial and error, or by sending off samples for testing, that you can be sure if it's suitable for your horse.

The trouble with grass (and the forage it is made into) is that it's everywhere and there is no easy way to check whether it is safe or not. Individual horses vary enormously in their ability to tolerate high sugar levels, different species of grass produce different levels of sugar, climate and growing conditions have dramatic effects, and how pasture is managed (is it artificially fertilized?) can also have an impact.

Old permanent pasture.

notoriously high in sugar and is very often planted as a monoculture, giving
on but to eat it; left to their own devices and given a choice, they will browse a
f plants, almost all of which are lower in starch and sugar (with a wider range of
n ryegrass. Horses that are sensitive will often cope much better on old permanent pasture with good biodiversity, so it's worth looking out for this type of grazing, or
sowing existing grazing with more horse-friendly species of grass if you can.

Ultimately the only way to find out how your horse reacts to your grass or forage is to
monitor his performance on the grazing and forage he is on. If you suspect a problem (and
the problem is so often the grass that I would always start with that), then the only way to be
sure that it's the cause of your horse's footiness is to take it out of the equation. Often horses
will improve rapidly – within days – once off grass or once the forage has been changed, but
you may need to give it a week to see a real improvement.

To confuse the picture even more, a horse that is footy grazing his field day and night over
the summer may be fine when eating the forage crop cut from the same field fed as haylage,
which is normally lower in sugar. It can certainly be tough to identify, let alone solve the
problem.

If in doubt, or if, as is often the case, your horse suddenly goes footy as the grass starts growing, I would start by reducing or removing all access to grass but keeping other forage the
same; if the problem persists, try soaking hay or using alternative haylage for another week,
and monitor him for improvement. If your horse improves, then you can gradually re-intro-
duce limited grazing – but look at the section later on for tips on how to make grazing safer.

The bad news is that if grass is a problem it can be a huge management challenge, especially over spring and summer. The good news is that there is a lot you can do to help; in addition horses that are highly sensitive to grass when they first come out of shoes can become
much more robust once they have tougher hooves, a few months or even a couple of seasons
down the line, and then life becomes a lot easier.

Paying very strict attention to the supplements you feed becomes even more important
once you know that grass is an issue, as high sugar levels in grass can also impact on the avail-
ability of key minerals, particularly magnesium. You may find, if your horse is particularly sensitive, or your grass particularly challenging, that you have to drastically restrict your horse's
access to grass in order to prevent footiness – but again there are many options.

Have a look through the next section for practical steps to take if you suspect grass is causing problems for your horse, but be aware that other dietary factors, including hard feed and
mineral supplements (or the lack of them) can also play a part. If you aren't sure where to start,
restricting grass and overhauling mineral supplements is a good first step.

It is worth pointing out that a horse's diet should consist predominantly of forage, of course,
so it's not a case of restricting forage, just finding out what sorts of forage are safe and healthy
for your horse. Our horses, on our relatively 'safe' grazing, are out at grass for at least twelve
hours a day even during spring and summer, but sometimes I have to restrict grazing for more
sensitive horses. However, all the horses here, whether rehabs or our own, have free access
all the time to our haylage (which is low sugar and high fibre) and that, along with a mineral
supplement balanced to add only what our forage lacks, forms the mainstay of their diet.

Minerals

The second biggest cause of footiness in horses, in my experience, is an inadequate level of
minerals in the diet. Horses get most of their minerals, along with most of their calories and

Horses vary in their ability to tolerate high sugar levels.

protein, from their forage, so of course if key mineral levels in your forage are low then your horse's whole diet will be low in those minerals too.

The commonest deficiencies in UK forage are copper, selenium, zinc and magnesium, so these minerals usually need to be added to the horse's diet. The simplest solution, which suits many horses and owners well, is to feed a mineral supplement that boosts these minerals.

Unfortunately very few off-the-shelf commercial supplements supply adequate amounts of these minerals, so I always suggest that owners go to one of the very few companies that make excellent supplements – my personal favourites are Progressive Earth's Pro Hoof/Pro Balance or alternatively Equinatural's Equivita. Progressive Earth have blazed a trail in equine nutrition for many years and are known for superb customer service (you can find them on the internet if you google Progressive Earth); Equinatural is another small, horse-centred business which is trusted by many; neither is cheap but both offer great value for money.

As well as a good mineral supplement it is important (and safe) to feed additional magnesium. Currently the most cost-effective and palatable way to do this is to feed magnesium oxide, the cheapest form of which is known as 'calcined magnesite'. Unlike other minerals, magnesium is safe to feed in relatively large amounts since horses will simply excrete any excess. Low magnesium levels cause a host of problems not limited to the feet, from spookiness to muscle dysfunction, so are something to be avoided. Magnesium does not taste nice and is best added to feeds at the very last minute. Most horses get used to it, but you may need to increase the amounts slowly, over a few days. I normally feed two 50ml scoops of calcined magnesite per horse per day, though you can reduce this amount over the winter if you wish. Conversely, if your forage is very high in calcium or sugar, you may need to increase this.

I also add salt to feeds, but you can provide a salt lick instead if you aren't sure whether your horse needs extra. Salt is one of the few substances that horses will self-select when they need it, so unlike other minerals it is possible to leave it up to them as to whether they eat it or not.

For the horses here, I mix their basic minerals (copper, zinc and selenium) plus the extra magnesium and salt with a good handful of micronized linseed and a 50ml scoop of brewers yeast per horse per day, which makes the whole feed more palatable. Horses in light to medium work simply have this added to a small amount of soaked grass cobs, unmollassed sugarbeet or Coolstance copra meal.

If you have ongoing problems even after your horse has been on a good, safe diet for a few weeks, then it is worth considering testing your forage. Although the mineral supplements mentioned will balance the majority of forage, there are occasions when deficiencies are so severe that bespoke mineral supplementation is needed. If this is the case you will need to have your grass or hay/haylage tested, and then balance minerals as the results require.

One point to make is that minerals are not palatable (at least the good ones aren't – most commercial supplements are dredged in molasses or sugar to encourage horses to eat them, but that's the last thing you want for a barefoot horse). However, most horses get used to eating them provided you introduce new flavours slowly and are persistent and consistent – don't fall into the trap of feeding some tastier alternative the first time your horse turns up his nose at his bowl of health food.

It helps if the other horses on your yard are also being fed a sugar-free bucket feed. I know from experience that even fussy horses will, once used to the feed, normally eat up, but when they are back on their home yard and surrounded by horses that are being fed molassed feeds, some rebel and, perhaps understandably, become picky about the healthier alternative.

Coming Out of Shoes

A horse may show sensitivity when it comes out of shoes. Some people assume that this is an inevitable reaction to not being shod, but in fact horses with healthy hooves and which are on a good diet typically come out of shoes and show little or no reaction to tougher terrain – so sensitivity is not inevitable. It is, however, a sign of an unhealthy foot, so if you have a horse like this the answer is, once again, to look at nutrition first. In fact the easiest and most successful way to take a shod horse barefoot is to thoroughly over-haul his diet first, and ensure that he has the

Healthy hooves are able to cope with tough terrain.

best nutrition possible for at least six or eight weeks before he comes out of shoes. This will allow most sound horses to come out of shoes with little or no foot sensitivity.

Metabolic Issues

For a horse that fails to improve on a good diet, my next step would always be to ask the vet to test for metabolic issues such as PPID (Cushings) or EMS, both of which can make horses extremely prone to sole sensitivity and laminitis. This is particularly the case if the horse becomes worse in the autumn, when hormonal levels change.

Trimming

Human intervention in the feet is another frequent cause of footiness. Sadly it is common for both trimmers and farriers to cut frogs and soles. It's sad because it's unnecessary, and although a horse with decent sole thickness and a robust frog may walk away, this type of trimming will leave a compromised foot sore. Please don't ever accept that horses should be sore following a trim – they shouldn't be!

Aggressive trimming is, of course, something to be avoided, but for one category of hoof even conservative trimming can be an issue. For instance, I would expect horses such as Dexter or Charlie, who have supportive wall deviations, to be totally comfortable even on tough terrain as long as they are on a good diet and on safe grass. However, if the supportive wall is removed during a trim, then the foot will be unbalanced – and it need not be an aggressive trim: for a sensitive horse losing even a few millimetres of hoof wall may be enough to cause a problem. This mechanical lack of support puts extra strain on the limb on uneven ground. In my experience this sort of medio-lateral imbalance frequently results in a shortened stride, worse on rough ground, which will look and feel under saddle exactly the same as a footy horse.

Many farriers and trimmers feel obliged to remove flare out of a mistaken belief that it is somehow damaging. In my experience this just isn't the case. If flare is supportive it should not be removed because it is essential for optimal medio-lateral balance. If, on the other hand, it is true flare – a hoof capsule deformation caused by white line damage, laminitis or similar

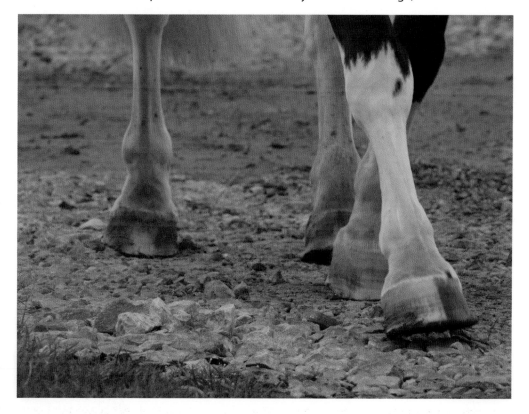

Any trim that compromises a good landing should not be repeated.

– then it will be so weakly attached relative to the correct, new hoof growth that it will never be strong enough to compromise the new growth. In the first case trimming is unsafe, in the second case it is unnecessary.

If a horse has pretty feet that are regularly trimmed but he is not totally comfortable over rough, uneven terrain despite being on a good, safe diet, then it might be sensible to stop trimming him – whether this is normally done by you or by a professional – just in case he needs support from hoof wall that is regularly being taken away. If he becomes steadily more capable over this sort of ground when not trimmed, but has 'flare' that never seems to disappear on its own, then it is likely that the 'flare' is in fact supportive.

Removal of supportive 'flare' will make a horse footsore, but the cause is completely different from dietary or metabolic-related footiness, where the discomfort is related to inflammation of the sole or laminae, in a way similar to laminitis. Footiness that results from the removal of supportive hoof wall seems to be the result of strain to collateral ligaments. I have seen on video footage that horses that land evenly with supportive 'flare' will usually land on the lateral heel if the flare is removed.

When we have rehab horses here that show this sort of tipping on landing, it is associated with collateral ligament strain on MRI. It would make sense that, if supportive flare is removed by trimming, then the foot will be unbalanced, forcing a one-sided landing and putting collateral ligaments under greater stress. It would not be surprising if this sort of strain were made worse on a hard, uneven surface. Moreover, where footiness triggered by sugars and starches is relatively quick to resolve once the trigger is removed, footiness relating to a lack of support and medio-lateral imbalance is slower to improve. It can take several weeks for the supportive structures of the hoof capsule to re-grow and enable the correct balance to be restored.

Other Causes

If you are still at a loss with a footy horse it is worth checking whether he has been wormed or vaccinated recently, as both of these can trigger footiness in sensitive horses.

Footiness caused by wormers can be slow to clear, particularly if you use longer-acting, combination wormers that are designed to remain effective for eight to twelve weeks. Although it is essential to have effective parasite control, there are, for the vast majority of horses, safe ways of achieving this without needing to sacrifice hoof health or performance.

For a start, wormers should be used only as and when required – the days of simply dosing your horse every six weeks regardless of whether or not he needs it are (or should be) long gone for responsible horse owners. A more targeted approach, using saliva tests to check for tapeworm and regular faecal egg counts to check whether worming is needed, is better for the horse and the environment and more effective. It should also reduce the risk of parasites developing resistance to the wormers we currently use.

Remember that even if your horse regularly has low or zero egg counts, it is important to use a wormer that targets encysted redworm annually.

The critical point to remember with any wormer is to avoid combination wormers, only to dose the horse with one active ingredient at a time, and to give a few weeks' break between different treatments.

Finally, it is possible that if a horse is suffering from a virus, or from ulcers within the gut, this will lead to footiness, although it is unusual. If you have exhausted all other avenues, then ruling these out is something you should discuss with your vet.

Pea shingle (5–10mm) is a comfortable surface for horses with weak feet.

CHAPTER 12

Further Troubleshooting

Increasing a horse's movement and work levels is an essential part of most rehabilitation, but as you might expect, the devil is in the detail. While the right work can make the difference between increasing soundness and ongoing lameness, the wrong work can rapidly make matters worse.

I am always alarmed when I see well-meaning punters online recommending exercise for someone's lame horse. While the plethora of advice on the internet can be a real boon and has saved many a horse and owner from a grim and gloomy diagnosis, it does need to be treated with caution. After all, someone who tells a good tale on social media about the wonderful progress their horse has made may have very different ideas to you as to what constitutes consistent work, or even a sound horse.

SAFE EXERCISE FOR REHABILITATION

The critical thing with exercise is to ensure that the work the horse is doing is good work – work that enhances his range of movement and leads to increased soundness without causing strain to healing injuries.

* **Allow as much free movement as possible**
Most horses will benefit from turnout even after injury, and it also helps to keep them relaxed. If a horse is likely to damage himself by galloping about, then you may need to restrict his turnout; but allowing him access to a track where he can mooch about quietly, or giving him a yard or small paddock that ideally he can share with a placid friend, is likely to keep him calmer and healthier, in the long run, than box rest, as well as making re-injury less likely.

We have had many horses come to us straight from box rest for rehab, but we have never had issues with horses re-injuring themselves when given access to our tracks. Once they have got used to being able to stretch their legs gently exercising on a track, where there are no wide open spaces to encourage high speeds, it's also that much easier to turn them back out in the fields without them going crazy.

* **Monitor how the horse is landing and loading his feet to help you determine the appropriate exercise level for him and what surfaces are likely to help him**
A horse that is landing toe first will not benefit from work on hard surfaces; he needs only gentle movement on conformable ground, which will minimize the damage his landing is doing to his tendons and ligaments, and will promote stimulation to strengthen the palmar hoof. Some movement is important as box rest will not give his feet the stimulus they need to

Amenable company is a great help in keeping horses calm.

change, but you should be very cautious as to how much you allow him, until a better landing has become established.

* Vary work so that the horse is not doing the same thing day after day

A mixture of work is best, and with most lameness rehabilitation the majority should be in-hand work at first. Once the horse has an established heel-first landing and is becoming steadily sounder, you can then build up to hacking out. If possible, it is good policy to start all work (both in the school and out and about) in hand, as most horses will need to build or rebuild topline before being ridden; long-reining or leading from another horse are good options for strengthening feet while helping to get the rest of the horse fitter.

* Ensure that there are regular breaks between work sessions to allow recovery

A safe rule initially is to allow one day off after every day of work. Once your horse is steadily improving you can start to introduce work on two days back to back, but I would not ask him to work for longer than this during his rehabilitation. As a rule I would not work a horse more than four alternate days per week throughout his rehabilitation period. Once he is fully sound and back in the same level of work as he was originally, you can work him harder – provided, as always, that you make changes slowly and consistently.

* **Make increases in work level or intensity gradual**

Only increase the level or intensity of work once you are happy that the horse is comfortable at the previous level, and has made a consistent improvement in soundness at the lower level. Don't forget that changing from in hand to ridden work is in itself a big step up for the horse. Personally I would want the horse to have been working happily for several weeks in hand before moving on to work under saddle.

* **When changing work levels, only change one thing at a time**

Only change one thing at a time when increasing the work level. So, for instance, you could add some faster work, or work of a longer duration, or work on a tougher surface, or work that is more intense (ridden, rather than in hand, for instance) – but you should only do one of these things at a time. Once you are happy that the increase has become an established and beneficial part of your horse's exercise level, then you can make a further change.

* **Be careful, but don't be over cautious**

No work can be as detrimental to horses as too much work. It's very common for owners to be tentative when beginning work with a horse that has been injured. While this is completely understandable, as an owner you need to find the balance between being too careful and not doing enough, and being too bold and doing too much. It's sensible to err on the side of caution, but try not to be too intimidated by the fear of re-injury. If you listen to your horse, respect his comfort levels, and keep a close eye on how he is landing, then you should be able to ensure that the work you are doing is constructive.

Don't forget that work is essential to keep hooves in top condition.

* **Don't let concern for your horse paralyse you both**

This is related to the previous point and I talked about it in more detail earlier. You need to ensure that your concern for your horse does not prevent you from working him effectively; you also need to ensure that your worry does not influence your horse and sap his confidence. After all, if he has been lame and sore for a long time he needs to trust that what you are asking him to do is going to make him feel better.

I usually advise owners to try and behave as if they are a kindly but no-nonsense nurse or teacher, sympathetic but reassuring, instilling in the horse confidence that the work you are asking him to do is good for him and will help him improve and become stronger in the long term. This will also enable him to relax, which is an essential precondition to him stepping out and working correctly.

FEEDING FOR MEDIUM OR HARD WORK

Most horses will get all the calories they need for light to medium work from good forage and a mineral supplement, but if you need to feed extra calories or protein then, as with mineral supplements, it is better to turn your back on manufactured bags of cubes, nuts and mixes and keep things as simple as possible. The other benefit of this approach is that you can easily isolate an ingredient if something does not suit your horse.

For horses in hard work I feed the same basics – minerals, magnesium, linseed and yeast mixed into soaked cobs, unmolassed beet or CoolStance copra meal – and simply add extra calories and protein.

The safest way to feed extra calories or protein to a barefoot horse is to add crushed oats (which are the cereal with the highest fibre and lowest starch), Coolstance copra meal (which is coconut based) or alfalfa pellets.

Oats are a good source of energy, and contrary to traditional beliefs I have never found that they cause horses to become excitable, although you should, of course, introduce any new feed slowly and gradually.

Coolstance is ideal if you want to increase protein levels or need slow-release energy for hunting or long distances, as it is high in oil and low in starch.

Alfalfa (also called lucerne) sometimes causes

Feed minerals to every horse; CoolStance is a safe way to feed calories and protein to those working hard.

controversy, but is a useful feed in the right circumstances. It can be a good source of additional protein or energy, but it is high in calcium and so can cause problems if you are already feeding forage that is high in calcium. If your horse becomes footsore soon after you start feeding alfalfa, then cut it out and try one of the alternatives.

You should, of course, vary the size of feeds depending on the horse and his work level, but keeping the basic feed the same and simply adjusting calories and protein means that it is easy to tweak the energy level of feeds while ensuring that every horse is always getting the essential minerals he requires, even when his workload varies.

Feeding this way is very safe for feet as you are avoiding the high levels of sugars and starches that you would be feeding if you use cubes or mixes. At the same time you can ensure that good doers, who need no extra energy, are getting the minerals they need for good health.

Very often if a horse is overweight his feed will be drastically reduced. This seems a logical thing to do, but the problem is that even fat horses on limited forage will probably need additional minerals, even if they get all the calories they need (and more) from their forage.

I don't feed chaff or bagged chopped fibre, as many of these products, even when sugar free, contain mould inhibitors that can trigger footiness in horses, and it is not worth the risk. Chaff used to be given as an addition to hard feeds, providing fibre to horses on restricted forage, but I prefer to ensure that horses have access to forage at all times; therefore adding any sort of chaff to hard feed is not necessary.

As with all feeds, if you are not sure whether a particular feed is causing problems, just exclude it and monitor your horse for improvement.

LAMENESS

I'll say right away that this section is not intended to be any substitute for veterinary advice, although that should be obvious. However, even after careful rehabilitation, there can be times when a horse seems to go backwards – he suddenly isn't quite as good as he was, or he just loses momentum for some reason. Finding out the reason for this change can certainly be a detective game, but I hope the ideas in this section will help you rule things in or out in a systematic manner.

*   Has anything changed?

Common problems have common causes. Changes in diet (particularly grass), wormers and vaccinations are the most usual causes of horses becoming short-striding or footy, so the first step is to rule these out.

A step up in work level, or lots of work on a tougher surface too soon can also set a horse back. If this is the case, simply going back to a lower level of work for a few days should do the trick.

*   Is your horse still landing correctly?

A horse that has lost a heel-first landing or good medio-lateral balance is immediately more prone to injury, so this is the next thing to check. Have a look at the chapter on hoof balance if you aren't sure how to assess this for yourself.

The good news is that even if your horse has lost good dynamic balance, it can be restored with careful work. The sections on exercise for rehabilitation have advice on introducing (or reintroducing) beneficial work.

*   **Does your horse have a weak frog which is making him reluctant to land heel first?**
Thrush or infections can easily take hold in a horse that is not landing heel first, and they make it even more difficult for the horse to improve how he is landing. If your horse has a sensitive frog or a split in the central sulcus (which runs down the middle of the frog) then you will probably need to treat it regularly to get rid of infection until it heals up.

There are plenty of off-the-shelf treatments you can use, but whatever you choose needs to be mild enough not to damage tissue. I prefer either medical grade Manuka honey or Veterinus dermagel applied daily and pushed in as far as possible, with a dollop of Sudocreme on top to help it stay in place.

*   **Is your saddle or girth impeding your horse's front limb movement?**
A horse coming back into work will often develop a bigger stride, and to do this he needs the full freedom of his shoulders and front limbs. It is very, very common for a saddle that fitted before the horse was injured to be tight and restrictive after rehabilitation.

You also need to check that the girth is not impeding the horse, as some horses will swing their front legs so far back that the elbow can come up against the girth. This is uncomfortable, and can cause a horse to shorten up in front, but a softer girth or one of a different shape should solve the problem.

If in doubt, particularly when you know the horse is landing well and has healthy hooves, work him with and without tack, and film his movement so you can see if his gait changes

Poor saddle fit or irritation from the girth can cause lameness.

once he is tacked up. I have seen a horse go from head-nodding lame to almost perfectly sound just with a change of saddle and girth, so it's worth ruling out ill-fitting tack as a reason for lameness.

As with every other profession, there are good saddlers and bad saddlers out there; your horse should be the ultimate arbiter of whether his saddle is a good fit, or whether it restricts his movement. And if your saddler disagrees with your horse, get a new saddler!

Get out and work those hooves!

CHAPTER 13

Anthropomorphism?

Throughout this book I have unapologetically referred to horses as having sense and feeling. I could spend hours watching our own horses, and I've known them for years. I can see when Felix is bored and gives me 'that look', which means he may take some gates off their hinges for the fun of breaking into forbidden fields; I am aware when something is worrying Charlie and he needs a bit of reassurance; I can spot when young Bryher is about to start pushing the boundaries with the other horses, and rough-housing as a way of amusing himself; it is unmistakable when Bailey is in a bad mood and about to take it out on someone else, usually quite unfairly, but that's just the way she is.

It seems obvious to me that horses have a clear awareness of who they are, and who their friends are, and they have complex relationships with each other and with us. My horses exuberantly greet a returning herd member, even after a year or more away, and he will slot straight back in as 'one of the gang', whereas a new horse will have to prove himself before he is fully accepted. They are capable of being friendly, curious, sad, contented, demonstrative, playful, wary, excited, unimpressed, bolshy, melodramatic, brave, patient or demand-

Do animals share human emotions? Yes, they do.

Fear, aggression, well-being, anxiety, pleasure are the shared feelings of a shared world.

ing – sometimes all on the same day. However, while most horse owners (and indeed, most equine professionals with their feet rooted in reality) will have had the same experiences as I have, and will acknowledge the self-evident truth of this, there will be some who read this and accuse me of anthropomorphism.

They would be quite right. The anthropomorphism in this book is not something I am going to deny or amend. Anthropomorphism is, of course, what we do when we 'attribute human traits, emotions and intentions to non-human entities'. It is an overwhelming tendency in the way humans behave towards all animals, and it is something that is even easier to do with the animals who share our lives, and whom we know intimately.

Up until fairly recently it was considered extremely unscientific to use anthropomorphic language, and I might have tried to curb my natural tendency to do so, but science is finally catching up with the truth which those of us who live closely with animals have always understood intuitively. In other words, we don't need to apologize for being anthropomorphic, because it turns out that emotions and consciousness aren't uniquely human after all. There is no problem with anthropomorphism because we are simply in recognizing in our animals and attributing to them traits, intentions and emotions that they really do share with us.

For anyone interested in reading more I would recommend Carl Safina's fantastic book *Beyond Words – What Animals Think and Feel*, which includes a thoughtful exposition of the science, as well as his own unique observations and conclusions about animal lives. I'll let him say it in his own words.

We never seem to doubt that an animal acting hungry feels hunger. What reason is there to disbelieve that an elephant who seems happy is happy? We recognize hunger and thirst while animals are eating and drinking, exhaustion when they tire, but deny them joy and happiness as they are playing with their children and their families. The science of animal behaviour has long operated with that bias – and that's unscientific. In science the simplest interpretation of evidence is often the best. When elephants seem joyous in joyful contexts, joy is the simplest interpretation of the evidence. Their brains are similar to ours, they make the same hormones involved in human emotions – and that's evidence, too. So let's not assume. But let's not bury evidence …

Elephants form deep social bonds developed through deep time. Parental care, satisfaction, friendship, compassion and grief didn't just suddenly appear with the emergence of modern humans. All began their journey in pre-human beings. Our brain's provenance is inseparable from other species' brains in the long cauldron of living time. And thus, so is our mind. So, do other animals have human emotions? Yes, they do. Do humans have animal emotions? Yes, they're largely the same. Fear, aggression, well-being, anxiety and pleasure are the emotions of shared brain structures and shared chemistries, originated in shared ancestry. They are the shared feelings of a shared world.

We can understand that the emotions we feel are shared by our animals, and I would not be at all surprised – in fact I would expect it to be true – that they understand that the emotions they feel are shared by us.

Index